from

THE DIARY OF PETER PARSON

I have never had a comfortable experience of God. When I say that I find him in life, it is rather that he finds me. When I grew out of my teens, it was not so much in loveliness that I became aware of him as in the meeting with life's demands, in the necessity for decision, in the affront of ugliness and slums and poverty.

When I try to sum up in nontheological language what religion means to me, I find it inevitably shapes itself into two words—responsibility and belonging. I am never able to shake free of the knowledge that I belong to life, that I cannot contract out of it; and that I am responsible, not merely to myself, to my neighbors and friends, but to God. And when I am true to these points, everything else in my life becomes significant and right. Nowadays I do not ask for emotional uplift; I find the more deeply involved I am in life, the more real God becomes to me.

THE DIARY OF PETER PARSON

THE DIARY OF
PETER PARSON

W. B. J. MARTIN

NEW YORK   ABINGDON PRESS   NASHVILLE

THE DIARY OF PETER PARSON

Published in Great Britain
under the title
FIVE MINUTES TO TWELVE

1957 © *MCMLVII by W. B. J. Martin*

Library of Congress Catalog Card Number: 58-7435

SET UP, PRINTED, AND BOUND BY THE
PARTHENON PRESS, AT NASHVILLE,
TENNESSEE, UNITED STATES OF AMERICA

This book is dedicated to

SHAUN HERRON

who *puts friendship first*

—— ACKNOWLEDMENTS ——

For the reprinting of copyrighted material I wish to make the following acknowledgments: The selection on page 17 is from *Up Stream—An American Chronicle* by Ludwig Lewisohn. Copyright R1952 by Ludwig Lewisohn. Permission of Liveright Publishing Corp. The poem on page 24 is from *The Variorum Edition of the Poems of W. B. Yeats,* ed. Peter Allt and Russell K. Alspach. Copyright 1958 and used by permission of The Macmillan Co. The selection on page 70 is from *The Later Ego* by James Agate. Copyright 1951 by Crown Publishers, Inc. Reprinted by permission of the publisher. The selection on pages 77-78 from *The Heathen Are Wrong* by Eugene Bagger is © 1941 by Eugene Bagger and used by permission of A. Watkins, Inc. The selection on page 81 by John Wren-Lewis from the *Hibbert Journal* is used by permission of the author. The selection on page 82 from *Letters and Papers from Prison* by Dietrich Bonhoeffer is copyright 1954 and used by permission of The Macmillan Co. The selection on page 107 from *Vitality* by Malcolm Spencer is used by permission of S.C.M. Press. The selection on page 112 by Bernard Eugene Meland is from *Faith and Culture* and is used by permission of Oxford University Press. The poetry on pages 122 and 170-71 from *For the Time Being* by W. H. Auden is copyright 1944 and used by permission of Random House. The selections on pages 125-26 from *Painted Windows* are by Harold Begbie, copyright 1922 and used by permission of G. P. Putnam's Sons. The selection on pages 141-42, and the poem on page 151 by Attila Jozsef, are from *The Invisible Writing* by Arthur Koestler, copyright 1954 and used by permission of The Macmillan Co. The poem "Soliloquy" on page 170 from *Collected Poems* by Edwin Muir is used by permission of Grove Press. The poetry on page 170 by Cecil Lay Lewis is used by permission of Harold Matson Co. The poetry on page 171 by W. H. Davies is from "A Great Time" and is used by permission of *The Saturday Review.*

—— FOREWORD ——

FOR MANY YEARS NOW IT HAS BEEN MY PRACTICE TO SPEND THE last half-hour of each day in writing up my journal. It has become almost as much a habit as switching off the light at my bedside, and perhaps it serves the same purpose—to reduce the glare in the mind. Putting the events and thoughts of the day on paper gives me freedom to get on with the business of sleep.

There is no fun and no point in keeping a journal if one is not ruthlessly honest. Neither is there much joy or profit to oneself if one is careful, judicial, balanced. Many of the entries recorded here reveal a mood rather than a settled conviction. I hope they will be none the less valuable for that.

Anyway, here, for what they are worth, are the uninhibited musings of a working parson, reflections and comments on the day-to-day encounters with his own church members, with non-churchmen, with fellow parsons, and reflections on his own failures and successes.

1

I COULD SEE HE WAS PUZZLED. HE HAD NEVER MET A PARSON AT such close quarters before. "How does one become a parson?" he asked. "What sent you into the church? What led you to devote your life to preaching?" Behind these polite questions I sensed others, less polite and more searching. "What makes people like you tick? What unconscious arrogance drives you to mount a pulpit and tell other people how to live? What gives you the right to shape their thought and conduct?"

He was a twenty-three-year-old Australian spending a couple of years in this country at a nearby university. There was something pagan about him, begotten perhaps of sun bathing, surf riding, and the open-air life of a thriving, young, materialistic society. It showed through his physique, his hard mental attitude, his frankness. He had arrived at the manse door bearing a letter of introduction from a friend. This was his third visit to the manse, but he had not yet been inside the church, nor did he show the slightest desire to enter it. It struck me that it would no more occur to him to attend a service of worship in my church than it would occur to me to enter a Jewish synagogue. It represented an alien world. But he was evidently enjoying his contact with a minister of religion. This was a new experience, and although I seemed to be an unusually open-minded parson, I was still a parson —a rare bird, a queer specimen.

I saw him off to the bus. His parting words were: "May I come to tea again when I get back next term? I'd like to hear more from you about that 'call' business."

Well, yes, he could come again by all means. I did not resent his curiosity. It was a welcome change from the take-it-for-granted attitude I was used to. My own church members showed no interest in my mental and spiritual processes. Perhaps they are too well-bred to ask personal questions—or perhaps they already know without asking what it feels like to be "called" themselves. But sometimes I suspect that they are a little afraid of asking fundamental questions through fear of being taken out of their depth. Anyway, it was a refreshing change to meet the probing curiosity of young MacLellan.

When he comes back next term, how much shall I tell him? How much *can* I tell him? Among one's fellow Christians one makes use of a kind of shorthand, but with a complete outsider everything will have to be spelled out in full. If I am perfectly frank about all the factors that went to make up my call to the ministry, how much will he be able to understand? Come to think of it, how much do I understand myself?

A "call" to the ministry is—or was in my case, and I do not flatter myself that I am unique—a curious mixture of motives, drives, inclinations, and repulsions, a tangled web of the respectable and the not so respectable, of idealism and self-seeking, of the desire to give oneself to God and the desire to exhibit oneself. No human action is entirely pure, and this one, though it bears the label "religious," is no less ambiguous than any other. Have I really the courage to lay bare the hopes and fears, the muddle of adolescent desires; to disentangle the genuine desire to serve the Christ who had caught my young life, from the scarcely acknowledged desire to make a career for myself, to escape from a frustrating industrial job? And if I can do it, will it be any use sharing it with anybody—least of all with MacLellan?

I resolve to have a shot at it. But for the moment, he's away and there are more urgent things to do. I hurry back to the manse to resume work on next Sunday's sermons. Now where was I? Oh, yes, "And as Jesus passed forth . . . , he saw a man, named Matthew, sitting at the receipt of custom."

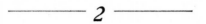

2

WOULD I GO TO CHURCH REGULARLY IF I WERE NOT A PARSON? Last month I sat in the pew for four Sundays as a listener. It did me good as both a man and a minister. But I was appalled by the dullness of the services. The preaching was competent, mildly interesting, helpful in a general way, but over all there was a thin spread of mediocrity—not a memorable phrase, a distinguished thought, and above all, no element of surprise. One had heard it all before, expressed in much the same way.

Ogden Nash described his method of versifying by saying, "What I do is to pick up poetry and bash its brains out against the sidewalk." I wish preachers were as violent with their sermon techniques. There seems to be a standard pattern of sermon— introduction, three headings, and conclusion. The congregation awaits the unfolding of this pattern with the dazed look of condemned men. And there is something more seriously amiss than the lack of expectancy: there is a sense of unreality. Truth does not fall into a standard pattern. Yet Sunday by Sunday the listener finds it presented in the same rigid framework. Can he escape the conclusion that the truth is being forced into a mold, cut down to size, hacked about in order to make a sermon out of it?

Why three heads? Charles Jefferson once preached a sermon

11

in Broadway Tabernacle with nine heads. He was dealing with the incident of the ten lepers, and his sermon took the form of questions addressed to the nine men who did not return to give thanks. Harry Emerson Fosdick was fond of the number six. "Six Ways of Telling Right from Wrong," "Six Ways in Which Modern Man Can Pray," are the titles of two well-remembered sermons. Personally I prefer a sermon with one idea, thoroughly hammered home, thoroughly probed and applied to ordinary life. The best preaching is vivid conversation. Conversation takes many forms and shapes.

Another pulpit convention, impressed upon budding preachers in theological colleges, has done much to make preaching dull. I mean the counsel to take only the finished product into the pulpit. My own homiletics professor used to say, "People are not interested in the shavings of your workshop; they want to see the finished article." He had evidently forgotten his boyhood and the immense fascination of watching men at work. Would the village blacksmith have gathered the crowd around the smithy door if he had merely displayed the completed horseshoe? Behind the professor's advice there was this element of truth: we are in the pulpit to preach not our mental processes but our convictions. But convictions have a history. They fight with a man, and he fights with them. Congregations have a right to know, and they would certainly be interested in knowing, how the fight took place. I think we ought to take our listeners into our confidence, even about the making of sermons and the struggles, hesitations, revisions, that have taken place before the final presentation. This is how Christ deals with us in the stuff of daily life, which includes for us parsons the making of sermons.

What I personally miss most on the rare occasions when I sit listening to a brother minister is the feel of a living man talking naturally about things that matter to him; of a man sharing his experience of God and life with an immediacy, directness, and urgency that is not a bit concerned with sermon structure.

3

THE OFFICIAL NOTE PAPER OF WORMWOOD SCRUBS PRISON IS headed "The permission to write and receive letters is given to prisoners for the purpose of enabling them to keep up a connection with their respectable friends."

It was reassuring to get this certificate of respectability today when the postman brought me a letter from a young fellow who is "doing time" in the Scrubs. He belongs to the open youth club our church runs for the benefit of the adolescents about our door. Despite his present address he is a fundamentally decent young chap who "happened" to have got into trouble, something involving the use of a motor lorry in a burglary. Naturally when I heard that he was inside, I sat down and wrote, not exactly commiserating with him, but on the other hand not in an "I-told-you-so" vein, but as a friend who desired to keep in touch with him. Maybe I should have underlined the lesson that his imprisonment was teaching him, but I assumed that it would need no underlining from me. So I made the letter as natural as possible, giving him news of the club and the fortunes of the football team, of which he was a keen member.

Now on two quarto pages I have his reply. It starts off: "I am sorry I did not answer you before, but you know what it's like in these places, you keep putting things off, at least that's what I do." I love this identification! But it also worries me. When I wrote to him, I tried to find some common ground. Actually this meant that I moved off my ground onto his. I wrote down to his level. I assumed that he would be interested only in personal gossip and sporting news. But is not this dishonest? It means that I am not giving him myself, but that part of myself which I think will be welcomed and understood. So when next I write, I am resolved to be natural: I will share with him, even at the risk of puzzling him, some of the concerns that are real and vital to me as a minister of religion. The club of which he is a member is very loosely connected with the church; there are no strings attached, no regulations requiring church attendance in return for billiards and table tennis. Nevertheless we always hope that some of the youngsters using the facilities offered them will recognize the motives from which we keep the club open and some day of their own free will will make their way to the chapel. It doesn't happen very often, and naturally this causes me some concern. I think that in my next letter I will express this concern to young Ronnie and ask him what he would do if he were in my place. After all, he knows the clientele of the club more intimately than I do!

Later

Ronnie writes: "Just a line in answer to your most welcome letter. I am not much of a brainy person but I am game to have a shot at anything. First of all I think (that's if you could spare the time) you should have a service for the club members only on a Sunday evening round about half past seven. I think that's the best time, but make sure it's for club members only, they don't like the old folks butting in. Most of your trouble will be to get the boys to

14

attend, the girls are not so bad, so use your loaf and get the girls together first, the boys will follow. . . . It's not easy for them though; they will get ragged by some who think it's a waste of time, and in that some I mean sometimes your best pal, that is true, I have had it happen to me. . . ."

So it goes on, an obviously sincere and happy letter; the boy is as pleased as punch to be at one with me in my job, perhaps even to help me see my way through a difficulty. Twice in the letter he uses, quite un-self-consciously, the phrase "the love of God," which for him obviously sums up the gist of Christian preaching. The bit about "your best pal" obviously came from the heart. I had already suspected that it takes a lot of courage for an East-End boy to wrench himself free from the customs and prejudices of his group; even if he wants to turn over a new leaf, he finds it difficult in face of the scorn and chaffing of his friends. He has to either carry them with him in a kind of group conversion or stay with them. There is the third, and heroic, way, but stronger personalities than Ronnie have hesitated long before stepping out into the loneliness of personal decision.

And then he gives me one piece of news which may help to explain many things in his recent behavior. "I have just seen the M.O., he tells me that I am going to get a glass eye put in right away. It will not quite match the other, but soon I shall be good-looking!" I wonder how far this physical disability accounts for his antisocial activities? How much of his supposedly "daring" behavior was compensation for his abnormal appearance, his desire to be "in" with the boys in spite of everything?

15

4

A THEOLOGICAL COLLEGE OUGHT TO BE A HOTBED OF HERESY.
Young men preparing to preach the gospel in the modern world
ought not to be such nice, safe boys, more eager to defend an
orthodox position than to submit it to the most rigorous criticism.
They, above all students, should be anxious to submit all things
to the honest doubt of their own minds, and if they have no doubts
of their own, they should be shown a few.

Perhaps things are better now, but when I entered a theological
seminary twenty-five years ago (the very seminary, I discovered
later, that had ejected Hazlitt and repelled "Mark Rutherford"),
I was thrown into the company of some forty young men preparing for the Nonconformist ministry. Ours was a residential college, located in an inner suburb of London. But though it proudly
claimed on its note paper to be a "divinity school of London University," we had virtually no contact with the varied and swirling
secular life of that university. The only students we met were
young men of our own kind, preparing for other branches of the
Nonconformist ministry, or, greatly daring, with the young men
preparing for the Anglican priesthood. For the most part we had
achieved Isaac Watts's ideal:

> A little garden walled around,
> Chosen of God, peculiar ground.

Not far away pulsed the busy life of the metropolis: the world
of the drama, music, painting, the world of youthful experiments
in thinking and living. The city proliferated with cults; men like
Shaw, Chesterton, Wells, were to be heard in public debate;
Orage, Middleton Murry, and other brilliant writers were speak-

ing to youth in the literary magazines, but of all this we were told nothing and we were not encouraged to find out. It would have been a waste of time, time stolen from our proper studies!

And truth to tell, most of us were not sorry that it was so. For the most part we liked the way we were shielded. We had no great urge to expose our meager ideas to the icy blasts of criticism or to throw our minds open to the world of ideas. Years later I came upon this passage in Ludwig Lewisohn's autobiography, *Up Stream—An American Chronicle,* in which he describes his experience as a teacher:

I stroll on the campus in spring. . . . The students are not disturbed at my approach. . . . I watch their faces. There is not a vicious face on the campus. I try to recall one among the hundreds of students I have taught. I cannot. Dull faces, vacant faces. Not one that expresses any corruption of heart and mind. I look about me again and watch for one face that betrays a troubled soul, a yearning of the mind, the touch of any flame. There is none. . . . I listen to their talk. It is of games, parties, examinations. Never of the contents of the tests. But of the practical fact that they have to be faced. Who has ever heard an eager argument among these students on any of the subjects —art, religion, economics, sex—that are supposed to employ the minds of men? Who has ever seen them keen about anything except (symbolically speaking) football and fudge? It is, as a matter of fact, considered rather bad form among them to show any stirring of the mind. It is considered "high-brow," queer, that is to say—different, personal and hence, by a subtle and quite mad implication consoling to stupidity and emptiness—undemocratic.

That chimes in with my own experience. I was one of the boys with a vacant, untroubled face. And there was only one member of the staff capable of bringing a touch of flame to it. He was a man obviously out of his element and regarded with grave suspicion by his colleagues. He was unreliable. He was invariably late. It was whispered that he drank. Students had been known to get a whiff of whisky off his breath at the ten o'clock lecture— but that might have been sheer imagination. He certainly did not fit into the pattern of a theological college; he was missing when public functions were afoot; he manifested obvious boredom on platforms; he talked about the rest of the staff with distaste. He delighted the students by sniping at the principal. "There's a man at the head of this institution who thinks that he has a private line to the Almighty, but he hasn't, you know." In short, he was a bounder. But he was alive. And as he paced the lecture room, he brought some of us alive; he shocked us into thinking; he questioned all the assumptions we had brought with us from our village Bethels and surburban churches. He roamed over heaven and earth in his sprawling lectures. "Any fool can give you facts," he often declared, "and any fool can remember facts. I'm here to give you ideas."

But alas, most of us wanted facts, facts with which to face the examiners, and we were impatient with him for withholding them. We were parsons in the making, and we had little time for exploring the universe. We wanted to pass examinations, and later on we would want material for turning out sermons.

Are things any better today? My own experience of modern theological colleges is limited. My impression is that the majority of theological students regard theology with boredom. It is a subject to be studied instead of illuminating all subjects. Ought not young fellows preparing for the Christian ministry to be so keen on theology that they eat, drink, dream, talk, and sleep theology? It isn't that the teaching is uninspired. I believe that we have as good a company of theological teachers today as we have ever had. Perhaps what the colleges need is a dog fish in the pond.

18

5

"YOU'RE A COWARD," WHISPERED MRS. YOUNG AS SHE SHOOK
hands with me at the end of this evening's service. It is not the
kind of remark with which she usually greets her minister. Nor-
mally I have no more appreciative and grateful listener than she.
But I was not altogether surprised; I guessed what she meant.
During Lent I have been preaching a course of sermons in the
mornings on aspects of the Cross, and I have varied this by de-
voting the evenings to a series on the Ten Commandments. Tonight I had reached the seventh, "Thou shalt not commit adultery."

The advantage of preaching a course of sermons is that some
subjects crop up naturally. It would be rather odd to preach on
adultery out of the blue. People might start speculating on the
reason for the preacher's sudden interest in the subject. But if it
arises naturally from the series, people come with minds prepared
and without any suspicion that the parson is getting at anybody in
particular.

But how is one to treat the subject of sex from the pulpit? The
average congregation is a mixed company. I looked down tonight
before giving out the text and noticed an adolescent boy who is
having a struggle with masturbation, a teen-age girl sitting beside
her mother in the family pew, a newly married couple making
their first appearance in church after the honeymoon, several
spinsters, and a sprinkling of grandparents. How is one to deal
in a general way with a subject that is so intensely personal for
each of us?

Mrs. Young called me a coward. Was she right? I had got
through the evening without once mentioning the word "sex."

19

This required a great deal of ingenuity, but I did it deliberately, because a word which is perfectly neutral in itself acquires a special aura when it is spoken from the pulpit. And so in speaking of adultery I had stressed the fact that the word has a wider reference than to what is commonly called "unfaithfulness in marriage." There are many kinds of infidelity, and the mental and spiritual withdrawals and betrayals are often more serious than the physical.

I may have been evasive, but on the whole I think I was right. There is a case for frankness from the pulpit. Religion has to be fully related to life, and the driving force of most normal lives is sex. There ought not to be any suspicion that the minister is involved in the conspiracy of silence. But there is another side to it. Perhaps it is not a bad thing that the church is one place in the world where the worshiper will be certain that the spotlight will not fall on sex, in an age and in a society where it is everywhere fiercely highlighted. It may be a good thing to feel that, though a powerful drive, it is only one among others, and that the problem is not that of "sex" in inverted commas, but the general problem of adjusting the personality toward God and of making oneself fully and creatively available to God for his glory and use.

Young Johnny will go out better equipped to meet the sense of frustration, of personal inadequacy and lack of purpose, which led him astray if I encourage him to accept the purpose which God has for his life than if I spoke directly upon that one symptom of his alienation from God, of his fear of being the self God wants him to be.

I think perhaps that the safest rule is to preach so that people in the pew come to realize that you are the sort of person who can safely be entrusted with a personal problem, someone who, though reticent, is fully aware of the strains and tensions under which he is living. Preach so that men and women realize that you have been where they are, that you are more concerned with them as persons than with the application of a law or a regulation. Above all, preach with the compassion of Jesus Christ in one's own heart.

6

THIS HAS BEEN A WEEK END OF CONTRASTS. ON SUNDAY EVENING, being off duty, I dropped into a little Anglican church near Piccadilly Circus. On Monday night I sat in the gallery of a theater round the corner in Shaftsbury Avenue. All drama was once religious drama. The theater sprang from the loins of the Church. Now apparently the roles are reversed. Men go to the theater to be purged with pity and terror; they go to church to be entertained.

They were certainly entertained in this church. The preacher was a visiting American, vividly autobiographical in style. Among other things he told us that he was in great demand as a counselor to youth. A young girl came to his vestry lately troubled by the problem of her inability to hold the boys. It seems that her dates were very seldom repeated. He diagnosed her trouble at once; the drooping lines around her mouth gave her away. So he advised her to spend ten minutes a day practicing a smile in front of the mirror. And in less than no time she was one of the most popular girls on the campus. I'm not making this up; I heard him say it with a smirk of satisfaction. But there was no suggestion that

21

behind the discontented expression there might lie a world of self-ishness, of trivial aims and an unworthy conception of love, calling for a radical act of repentance and reorganization. I naturally expected that the congregation realized that he was talking rubbish and would emerge spluttering with indignation. But the ones I heard were cooing with appreciation and praise.

The gallery at the Shaftsbury Avenue theater would have booed such nonsense. As it was, they were obviously gripped by Graham Green's play *The Living Room*. He had paid them the compliment of treating them as adults. His theme was in some ways not far removed from that of the preacher's: a young girl in love with a man much older than herself. The subject was not a religious one, although the central character was a crippled priest, and there was some incidental discussion of Roman Catholicism, but it was a secular subject treated by a deeply religious man from a religious point of view.

The church that tolerates piffle from the pulpit deserves its empty pews. The unforgivable sin in a preacher is triviality. Better anything than that—wrongheadedness, ignorant dogmatism, fanaticism. They do less harm in the long run than triviality.

7

TOM KENT CAME IN TONIGHT TO TELL ME THAT HE HAD FINALLY decided to offer himself for the Christian ministry. For the past ten years he has been holding down a well-paid administrative job but has been feeling increasingly restless. He is a brilliant fellow with an Oxford degree, a fine presence, and a good voice. I congratulate him on his decision, but I cannot help feeling a little uneasy. Tom gives me, and no doubt he will give others, the impression that he is more interested in ideas than in people. There is something a little inhuman about his brilliance, as though he were glad that he has a good case to argue and that he is happy in arguing it. It is the same impression that Douglas Paton gives me on the rare occasions when I listen to him preaching in his famous pulpit. All through the first part of the service he seems impatient to get down to the business in hand; during the singing of the hymns he is obviously restless and straining at the leash. Only when he at last rises to announce his text is he completely happy and at ease. And the unworthy thought has more than once occurred to me that he is more anxious to put his sermon across than to come into living fellowship with the men and women there before him.

I think it is fatal always to be preaching on "Prepare ye the way of the Lord." There is another text in Isaiah which calls for treatment by us, "Prepare ye the way of the people." Our congregations are in no doubt that we are on God's side; ought they not to feel that we are on their side too? To let men know that we understand and share the plight they are in, that we realize fully the anguish out of which their questions arise, is as necessary as to announce God's offer and demand: "Cast up the highway; gather out the stones; lift up a standard for the people."

8

The friends that have it I do wrong
Whenever I remake a song,
Should know what issue is at stake:
It is myself that I remake.

YEATS WAS EXPRESSING WHAT EVERY POET, WRITER, PAINTER, knows—that to make any work of art is to remake oneself. The satisfaction of writing sermons, to compare small things with great, is partly the artist's joy in creation, the creation ultimately of one's own life. The sermon is made to be preached, but the act of making it is an affirmation of one's own life, an attempt to identify oneself, to impose a pattern on the raw stuff of one's own experience.

That is why there is little satisfaction in preaching old sermons; they arrest and petrify one's development. The danger of being an itinerant preacher or a traveling evangelist is that there is little inner growth. One becomes more and more expert at expressing the same thing; technique develops, but the content remains static.

When Rainer Maria Rilke was urged to undergo psychoanalytical treatment, he resisted it. "You probably know," he wrote to a friend, "that Gebsattel is working with my wife since the spring; with her the problem is different, her work (sculpture) has never helped her, while mine from the beginning has been a kind of self-treatment." Perhaps if theological students were taught to regard themselves as artists and not as technicians, there would be less necessity for recourse to the psychologists. An

American friend tells me that the proportion of men in the semi-
naries who have to seek psychological help is alarming, something
like 50 per cent. "The infinite variety of problems confronting
theological students continues to amaze me," wrote another friend
lately, the dean of students at a large midwestern institution, "and
I sometimes wonder how we manage to turn out any preachers at
all." In my view their work should help them. If they were poets
and seers rather than religious salesmen, instead of developing
the salesman's ulcers they would be engaged in a perpetual process
of inward healing.

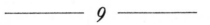

9

ALAN FULHAM CONFESSED, RATHER BOASTFULLY, I THOUGHT,
that he has given up reading theology. Now in his twenty-fifth
year as a pastor he finds fiction, biography, and travel reading
more suggestive for his work as a preacher than theological tomes.
His technique of presentation has improved, but the content of
his thought has remained static.

I stroll round his well-stocked shelves. They are gay with
the dust covers of modern novels, weighted down with important-
looking biographies of statesmen and politicians. I envy him. This
man is in touch with world events, with the thrilling, youthful
world of exploration and physical adventure. But on closer inspection I have doubts. I look in vain for the life stories of men who

have pushed back the frontiers of men's minds, biographies of people like Berdyaev, or Freud, or Marx. I suspect that what Alan is after is illustrations for sermons. What he gets out of memoirs and travel books are new ways of dressing up old truths. I get the impression as I listen to him in the pulpit that he has become more expert at saying the same old thing. I feel that the lives of politicians, explorers, ecclesiastical statesmen, are there to be mined for the anecdotes they can yield and that the theology has not moved forward since Alan left college.

My suspicion is confirmed when I notice the complete absence of modern poetry. In common with a great many other "readers," Alan dismisses modern poetry as unintelligible. What he really means is that it is unquotable. It does not lend itself easily to homiletical exploitation. The most one can get out of T. S. Eliot or W. H. Auden are significant lines. The older poets are more immediately intelligible; their verses can be used with greater effectiveness as perorations. But I doubt whether any preacher can call himself modern, can be in touch with the modern mind, who is cut off from the poets of today. They can give him something more vital than improving sentiments. They can give him an entirely new perspective from which to view the world, a heightened awareness of the situation of man in the modern world.

The poet is the super-sensitive, the super-perceptive, and the super-expressive one, the first to feel the strain, the wrong, the lie, the nastiness and the dearth, and the first to weep, to warn, to rebuke, to rebel . . . and also, the first to perceive the new promise, the hope, the shareable vision, incarnate in a single act or word, or in a life.

If a man shares the travail and the vision of the poets, he is not likely to find theology dull or useless. He may find much of the theology he learned at college a quarter of a century ago irrelevant, but the new questions, the new illumination which the best of our poets cast on the predicament of modern man, will send him shaken and eager to those theologians, like Barth, Brunner, Tillich, Niebuhr, and Nels Ferré, who, each in his own way, have an answer to the plight of man in the midtwentieth century.

But Alan is not in such bad shape as another minister into whose study I was admitted the other day. There was hardly a book on his shelves that was not either a book of sermons, sermonic material, or potted illustrations. There were bound volumes of the *Christian World Pulpit,* several copies of the American annual which provides sermons for every Sunday of the year, fifty children's addresses, and outlines for week-night services. I knew the owner of these books to be a melancholy man, whose people found him a dull preacher. And no wonder! How can a man be anything but a dull preacher, however bright the illustrations he has culled from other people, if his own mind has stopped working? The man who has the courage to read the New Testament for himself, to look at it with his own eyes and to report what he sees there with his own tongue, is a creative artist, however flat-footed. But if he is afraid to trust his own judgment, he becomes simply a homiletical joiner, piecing together prefabricated material. I say nothing of the religious side of all this; simply as a craftsman the man who depends upon other people's insights and illustrations loses the thrill of being an artist. Inevitably, of course, it must also dull his moral and religious response to the God of truth and creativity.

It all comes back to the theological college. Whatever else a man should or should not learn there, he should have learned to read. Something is drastically wrong if a man can spend three years in the company of theological teachers without catching the infection of reading, reading in the sense of pondering, wrestling with great ideas, and without experiencing the joy of presenting one's own vision.

———— *10* ————

TRUE TO HIS PROMISE YOUNG MACLELLAN, THE AUSTRALIAN student, turned up to tea today. I half hoped that he had forgotten his intention of probing my "call" to the ministry and tried to head him off by talking about his recent trip to Paris and his future plans, but he was not to be deflected. "You promised to tell me what made you become a parson," he said. "Please do; I'm really anxious to know what it feels like to be a minister and what goes on in a man's mind and heart when he first experiences a pull to the pulpit."

So I poured out another cup of tea and pushed the ashtray toward him. "Imagine, if you can," I began, "a boy brought up between the wars in an industrial town in Wales, where the church was the most real thing on the landscape, much more real for most of its inhabitants than the steelworks and the factories that stained the atmosphere. Everybody I knew, my immediate family, my neighbors, my schoolboy friends, were all church-goers or people who apologized for not going to church. As for me I went three times a Sunday—morning and evening service and

28

afternoon Bible class, and I frequently attended the Wednesday evening prayer meeting as well. I did not go because I was forced to go; I went because it was part of the pattern of my life. I went as I went to school, but more eagerly. As a matter of fact, I remember very little about my schools, but the influence of the church simply as an educational factor was decisive. The church was my university. It was from the pulpit that there sounded forth the notes of great literature. My minister was a magnificent reader of the Scriptures, a natural actor who brought out the poetry in the psalms and the drama of the narrative. It was from his lips that I first heard the names of Keats, Browning, Shelley, Wordsworth, and Tennyson—from him and not from my school-masters, who seemed to be more interested in their gardens and fishing trips than in literature. Not in the inky-fingered atmos-phere of the examination room, but in church, where men and women of all ages gathered to confront the issues of life, poetry served as an illumination of that dark, groping, sin-stained, and heroic life that we all shared. Music, too. The first, and for a long time, the only music I heard was played on the church organ. I was early introduced to Bach and Handel, though not by name. I was simply given the best as though it were part of my birthright. All this, together with the vision of a good life—not a life of stereotyped blamelessness, but a life of moral adventure and spiritual discovery—was mine from my very earliest days. And just as in a university the lectures are but a prelude to conversation and debate among one's peers, so every Sunday evening service was followed by a symposium. There was nothing organized about it; five or six young fellows (girls were out!) knotted to-gether in a local ice-cream parlor or walked out into the sur-rounding country and talked endlessly about religion, sex, poetry, and socialism. Nothing arose directly out of the sermon we had just heard, but unconsciously it set the pace and the tone of our discussions.

"Remember that background," I said, "and then perhaps you'll understand why I thought my minister was the most wonderful man in the community and why I both admired and envied him. Not only was he the most cultured man in our little town, but he was the only person with real leisure to read and enlarge his mind. The glimpse of his book-lined study was a peep into another world. Small wonder, then, that the thought of becoming a minister early seized my boyish mind; I dreamed of it as other boys dreamed of becoming engine drivers or explorers; I played preacher to my younger brothers and sisters, mounting the kitchen chair for a pulpit and holding them spellbound with eloquent perorations!

"There was a large element of exhibitionism in all this, of course. It had little to do with religion. I wanted to hold the center of the stage, and the only stage I knew was the pulpit. One of my recurring daydreams was of being present at a Sunday evening service in our crowded auditorium. The people were gathering and settling down, waiting expectantly for the preacher to emerge from the vestry and mount the pulpit steps. The sacred hour struck, but no preacher emerged. Presently three or four of the officials held whispered consultation, and the eyes of the leader sought me out in my accustomed seat in the gallery. Would I be good enough to take the minister's place? Naturally I had a sermon already written out and tucked away in my pocket, waiting for just such an emergency as this. Alas, the dream remained a dream. The minister never let his congregation down, and so I was denied my chance of stunning the congregation with my eloquence.

"Later on I abandoned all thoughts of being a minister. There

30

was nothing in my background or family tradition to encourage it, and the practical difficulties of a college training and financial stringency at home made it imperative to seek a job in a local factory, which I entered at the age of fourteen. From fourteen to twenty my adolescent *Sturm und Drang* was played out against the double backcloth of factory and church. It was the church that held me, however. There I interpreted my experience; there I encountered the understanding and love that reinstated me in my self-respect after bouts of playing the fool; there I was regularly brought into living encounter with the personality of Jesus, and there I gradually learned to recognize the claim of God upon my life and to respond to that claim in service, in responsible living, in deeper personal relationships.

"At twenty-four I was holding down a fairly responsible job in the drawing office of the firm I had entered at fourteen. Private study four nights a week at the Technical College and a pleasant, obliging manner had brought me to what outwardly seemed the beginning of a good career. But I knew, if nobody else did, that as a draftsman I was a failure. Engineering was not in my blood. And so suddenly one day I walked into the manager's office and tendered my resignation. I was going to be a minister. I wanted to devote my whole time to the Church, which had meant so much to me. How much of this decision sprang from a sincere desire to serve humanity through the Church, and how much sprang from my realization that I would never be any good in the job I was doing; how much of it sprang from the knowledge that entry into the ministry was—and is—the least arduous and expensive way of obtaining a university education and of entering one of the learned professions, and how much sprang from a genuine conviction that the world needs the religion of Jesus Christ more than it needs technical efficiency, who can tell?

31

I certainly cannot. As I look back, the life that I presented to the service of the Church and to Jesus of Nazareth was a muddled mixture of motives—some good, some bad. All I know is that God seems to have respected what was good and somehow turned it to use; gradually he has dealt with the unworthy, either using it to make me more understanding of similar young people or else in his mysterious mercy breaking it down and refining it . . ."

"There are a dozen points I'd like to take up with you about that," said MacLellan, "but I don't want to argue. It was nice of you to be frank and so autobiographical. If you'd told me that you'd heard a voice from heaven, I would have drunk your tea and inwardly spewed you out. But about the personality of Jesus being more . . ." "No, no," I cried, "that's enough for one afternoon. Come back again and we'll talk theology some other time."

11

YESTERDAY ALEC ROSS OFFERED TO LEND ME A NEW LIFE OF Robert Burns, but hoped I would not be shocked by it. Tonight young Laurie, who is a cub reporter on *The Sentinel,* was enthusiastic in his praise of a new novel, but hesitated about commending it to me because of its strong language and its revelation of the seamy side of life. I was amused both by their anxiety to shield me from "brutal reality" and by their obvious concern to take my worldly education in hand.

Where do they think we preachers live? In an ivory tower, sheltered from "the facts of life"? We may look innocent enough in our dog collars, and we may be shielded from the roughage of constant bad language and smutty talk, but I dare say that the average minister learns more of the sordid side of life, gets more personally involved in the mess and muddle of sex in his pastoral work, than the average businessman in his congregation is likely to do in his working contacts.

I don't keep a "casebook," but as I go back over my old diaries, certain names scorch my mind, bring back scenes of harrowing confession and humiliation. When people regard me as puritanical because I do not joke lightly about sex, they are not to know that three nights ago a young man sat in my study confessing that he dared not go to the lavatory without a Bible to place between his knees, that in every church to which I have ministered there have been tragedies caused by unbridled and perverted physical demands. Homosexuality has recently become a public issue, but few pastors have not encountered young men in their congregations, and those sometimes of the very finest and most sensitive spiritual sort, whose love life has become "abnormal." Other people may talk about the "problem of homosexuality"; we pastors know that there is no general problem, there are only particular cases; that there is no one cause for this inversion, but many; that one young man may be seeking the father he has never known, another coping with a deep psychic wound, yet another evading the responsibility that normal love, leading to marriage and family, inevitably brings. As for breakdowns in marriage, we pastors are acquainted with the strains of incompatibility, the clandestine "affair," not as interesting situations in a novel but as events involving many hours of argument, persuasion, probing,

33

prayer, leaving us limp and exhausted. No wonder we do not joke easily about marital infidelity!

Besides, a minister's reading is not confined to devotional manuals and theological tomes. He knows something of Freud and may even have read the Kinsey Report, but above all, he has looked into his own heart with the aid of a more searching light than any psychologist is likely to offer him. He knows what it is to cry with Peter, "Depart from me; for I am a sinful man, O Lord."

—————— *12* ——————

WOULD I BE A BETTER MAN IF I WERE NOT SO UNIFORMLY NICE to everybody? I have a certain reputation for suffering fools gladly, for seeing the best in people and for treating them all with patient understanding. Naturally I get no credit for this; it is attributed to my sunny disposition! Few people suspect the discipline I impose upon myself, or how often I am tempted to call fools by their proper name, or what a relief it would be to indulge in a good telling-off. I like to believe that the natural man in me has been somewhat modified by Christ. But now and again I am not altogether happy about it. I wonder whether this deliberate and painful adjustment to other people is not having a weakening effect on my own character; whether I am not in danger of losing my own identity, of having no real, strong central self, but only a shifting series of selves. And the trouble is that I suspect that my unfailing tolerance and understanding are not always the genuine articles. Perhaps it is less a matter of loving people than of soliciting their approval. I shrink from the thought of being disliked by anybody. This, I am sure, is a weakness; a man ought to have enemies if he has strong convictions.

And yet, to do myself justice, there is more to it than that. I do genuinely desire to enter into the lives of other people. I cannot bear to be shut out. And that is precisely what happens when one meets people with judgment, censure, condemnation, even when it is deserved. Once a man feels that you have made up your mind about him, that you are henceforth meeting him, not as a person but as an offender who has failed to measure up to some standard, his impulse is to avoid you. So I try to hold myself open to every point of view, to approach every individual as a special, unrepeatable problem, and this inevitably gives my own life the appearance of muddle, contradiction, and softness. I see both sides of every question, appreciate the difficulties a man is facing even better than he does himself. I should make a very indifferent prophet. The prophet lays about him, scorning evasions and compromises. But I am a pastor, whose instinct is to see the difficulties and to share them.

But this looks dreadfully like playing a part. One is the mourner among mourners, the life and soul of the party, the adolescent among adolescents, the family man. Which is the real me? Last night I sat in with an anxious and worried parent. I saw, I really entered into, his anxiety for young John. An hour ago young John was here, and I entered just as deeply into his adolescent restlessness and sympathized with his desire to break out of the mold in which his decent, careful family want to keep him. And so it goes on. I know the apostle Paul has words of counsel on this point, but alas, I am no Paul.

I know, too, that I would be a more acceptable preacher if I were less sensitive to persons. Congregations like to be told and even enjoy being told off; they like clear-cut solutions, final and authoritative answers. But I refuse to pander to their desire for verbal thrashings and for premature solutions.

13

THE POSTMAN HAS JUST DROPPED IN A REMINDER OF THE Ministers' Fraternal which meets next week at the home of Dr. Griffin. I enter the date in my diary—with a sigh. I shall go. I always go, on principle. I think fraternals are excellent institutions. How else are ministers to meet for the free and frank interchange of ideas, to discuss the latest theological opinion, or to share the secrets and problems of the preacher's craft? In practice, however, fraternals rarely live up to expectation. And the main trouble is that men in the ministry are reluctant to think aloud in one another's presence. We are all so guarded, so cautious, as though we foresee an occasion when we shall be called to account for something we blurted out in the unbuttoned mood of the moment.

When I stepped out of college into my first charge, I imagined that the monthly fraternal would continue the pattern and the atmosphere of the students' common room. I was soon disillusioned. We were not students any more, uncommitted to anything but the search for truth, eager to subject all the bases and assumptions of our thought to radical examination, willing to give mental hospitality to any idea, however wild and fantastic it might seem at first blush. Now we were men with the responsibility of the preaching and pastoral office. Although we met in the privacy and informality of a manse drawing room, we carried into it the gravity, not to say the pomposity, of the vestry.

I have belonged to some half-dozen fraternals in my time. The pattern differed widely in each case. In one district we met simply for tea and chat, usually ecclesiastical gossip, with a side glance at any local issues that demanded scrutiny or protest, like the opening of Sunday cinemas. We reported on congregational experiments, enlisted one another to speak at women's meetings or anniversaries; sometimes we even got to the point of commenting on a book that had recently appeared. But in general the conversation remain obstinately trivial and impersonal. In another group to which I had the privilege of belonging, we met with the stated purpose of reading the Greek Testament together. But the most stimulating company to which I ever belonged was one that met during the war in the East End of London. The fact that we were living in the most heavily blitzed area of London and that it was uncertain whether we would meet again, no doubt contributed to our openness to one another and to the urgency with which we discussed theological and social questions. But there was the further fact that each of these men, with one exception, had a first-class mind; they were men who sought to serve Christ in the hardest places of the field. Perhaps, too, the fact that we belonged to different branches of the church had something to do with it. Herbert, for instance, was a Quaker—a big-boned Yorkshireman incongruously set down in the slums of London to care for Cockney kids as warden of a Friends' social center. Inevitably he was a pacifist, with a quivering social conscience, always urging

37

us to show our Christian concern in practical ways. Philip was
a Baptist, in charge of a fundamentalist congregation, who eked
out his miserable stipend by writing articles for millenarian and
evangelical papers we had never heard of. But though he worked
within a narrow framework and his mind was naturally analytical,
his spirit was truly catholic. He assumed that we were as sincere
as he was, and so he entertained all our wildest and most "liberal"
notions with courteous gravity. The Methodist in our group was
a genial, scholarly man, who seemed to be wasting his gifts in
the administration of a bustling central mission. Away from his
soup kitchens, his nurseries and clubs, he seemed to revel in the
opportunity for hard and austere thinking. And we had a Uni-
tarian, a boyish, handsome young fellow, who put question marks
to all our beliefs, but who had an unquestioning belief in reason,
for which, you may be sure, he came under fire. One advantage
of this mixture, in which none of us belonged to the other's denomination, was that there was no temptation to play safe for
the sake of future prospects. William Miller told me a naughty
story of a certain Presbyterian minister in a Northern city, a
young man who was obviously "going places" in the denomination. He was seen to poke his head round the door of a theological
club in that city. He took one swift glance at the men assembled
there, decided that there were no future moderators present,
and tiptoed away! Well, there was no kudos or prestige to be
gained from belonging to our little circle; we were all on a level
and all willing to be as freakish, daring, or timid as the mood
dictated.

One of my standing disappointments with fraternals is the
absence of interest in the sheer craft of preaching. Get into a
circle of poets, painters, or musicians and there is endless, eager
discussion of form, schools, new works, and the willingness to

pass round one's own work for criticism and comment. But preachers, who believe theoretically in community, are in the main rank individualists. They are inhibited by a false idea of inspiration and of the sacredness of their office. A man must be true to his own vision, but the expression of it, the most effective presentation of what he has been permitted to see, is not sacrosanct. Again and again I have heard ministers defend their cagey individualism by comparing themselves with the prophets. The prophet, they say, did not go into committee. But the prophet was not the stark, isolated figure they make him out to be. He was firmly set within the context of his nation. He was often part of a school of prophets.

Well, I shall go to the fraternal next week, hoping as usual that the visors and armor will be thrown aside and doing my little part to deepen the sense of I and Thou.

14

YOUNG MACLELLAN, WHO WAS SO ANXIOUS TO HEAR ABOUT MY "call" to the ministry, actually turned up at church last night, "Tell me," he asked urgently when he came round to claim his tea at the manse, "did you really mean what you said last night? Frankly I didn't think much of your sermon, but when I listened to you praying from the pulpit, I found myself rather moved. It's a long time since I heard anybody pray, and though I felt it rather indecent to eavesdrop, it seemed to me that you had something. But it is so difficult to be sure. You are probably used to talking like that. Is God so real to you that you can genuinely thank him?

'We thank thee for speaking to us in the events and decisions of our daily life.' That's one phrase you used. Does he really speak? 'We thank thee for the experiences that make us very sure of thee.' That was another phrase you used. What are those experiences? Do the secular experiences of daily life really become religious experiences for you?"

As I reflected on this question, I remembered with shame the many times such phrases as he quoted had rolled glibly off my tongue, not because they corresponded to anything real in my immediate experience but because they were reminiscences of something I once knew. Or because my mind was tired and it snatched at any familiar form of words. Sometimes, too, I had been guilty of sheer phrasemaking, delighting in words almost for their own sake. And often when I had no experience of my own to offer up to God, I had contented myself by offering up what I hoped was the experience of other people there in the congregation.

When he saw my hesitation, MacLellan half-withdrew his question. "I'm sorry if I seem cheeky, but I really would like to know. This is more important to me than you perhaps suspect."

"No, it's all right," I said, "but I was just thinking that every trade has its dangers, and the parson's occupational disease is talking beyond his experience. Sometimes we preachers are guilty of using words two sizes too big for us. I may have been doing that last night; if I was, forgive me."

"What you said last night is not exactly the point," he answered. "However inflated the words may have been, there was something behind them. It's that something—religious experience—that I want to know about. Do you really have an experience of God breaking into your life, as your prayers seem to suggest?"

Of what are commonly called "mystical experiences" I can

THE DIARY OF PETER PARSON

report very few. The first moment of genuine religious feeling I can remember with any vividness is a feeling of concern and guardianship for two friends in my class at school. I felt that I had a responsibility for them, and when Noel started swearing or Len began to frequent the billiard saloon, a rather disreputable place near the school, it seemed to me that I was being challenged, that my friendship, because it was impure and undedicated, was partly the cause for their behavior. It sounds priggish, I dare say, and undoubtedly I was a little prig at the age of twelve, but I believe that God was within and behind the sense of responsibility and the desire to be worthy. A year or two later I had a rather different sort of experience. Late one evening I left the scout camp and took a solitary stroll along the headland. All day long I had been working, playing, cooking, and singing with as nice a bunch of lads as I ever hope to meet, but now some impulse, some unrecognized need, drove me to withdraw from them. I stood for half an hour looking out to sea.

> The holy time is quiet as a Nun
> breathless with adoration.

There was a full moon, I remember, and no doubt it all made a romantic setting for an adolescent boy. But it was something more than the sheer beauty of the scene that brought tears to my eyes. I was moved there and then to offer myself to God, because I was aware of him within the beauty, challenging the ugliness of my life. As I looked out upon a world of loveliness, I was aware of Another looking back at me and addressing me personally out of the heart of that loveliness.

So it has always been. I have never had a comfortable experience of God. When I say that I find him in life, it is rather that he finds me. When I grew out of my teens, it was not so much in loveliness that I became aware of him as in the meeting with life's demands, in the necessity for decision, in the affront of ugliness and slums and poverty.

When I try to sum up in nontheological language what religion means to me, I find it inevitably shapes itself into two words—responsibility and belonging. I am never able to shake free of the knowledge that I belong to life, that I cannot contract out of it; and that I am responsible, not merely to myself, to my neighbors and friends, but to God. And when I am true to these points, everything else in my life becomes significant and right. Nowadays I do not ask for emotional uplift; I find the more deeply involved I am in life, the more real God becomes to me.

15

IF I HAD TO WEED OUT MY LIBRARY, I SHOULD BEGIN BY THROWING out the preachers and the actors. I have over a thousand biographies and autobiographies on my shelves—poets, philosophers, novelists, men of action. I am of the opinion of Robertson Nicoll that no biography is entirely worthless. It is a curious thing, however, that the least satisfactory self-revealers are the clergymen and the actors. When they put pen to paper, they have scarcely anything interesting to say about themselves. About other people, yes; about events in which they have taken part, but about themselves they are dull. Reading an actor's life is like reading his press cuttings; reading a preacher's life is like reading his obituary notice.

Why is it? Even the very best, the most widely acclaimed, biographies of preachers, like that of Phillips Brooks, or Dale of Birmingham, or Alexander Whyte, leave you curiously uninformed about the man himself. Compared with the poets, for a contrast, how reluctant they are to offer us the hospitality of their private lives. Is it, I wonder, that parsons are always on duty, fearing to say anything that would lead the young astray or to suggest that the message by which they moved their thousands was delivered through a flawed instrument? I am sure they are wrong about this. The result of leaving out mental and spiritual and physical struggles, of presenting themselves always in their moderatorial robes or clerical collars, is to suggest to the young that they are deficient men, a kind of third sex, neither men nor women but parsons, with a correct but thin-blooded inner life, with senses that do not thrill or throb to the rich sights and sounds of God's world.

Or perhaps the reason is that preachers deal so much in generalities like "sin," "evil," and "doubt," pushing on without particularizing or probing them, whereas the poet is nothing if he is not concrete. Anyway, I know that I get more spiritual illumination and help from a book like Pierre Emmanuel's autobiography, *The Universal Singular,* or W. B. Yeats's life than from any preacher's life. For candor, though, I must single out L. P. Jacks. His was the first autobiography that gave me the feeling, Here is a completely fearless cleric, one who believes that truth can stand on its own bottom.

As for actors they seem to have no inner reality at all. They are so concerned with getting into a part, with presenting Shaw's Dauphin or Ibsen's Solness, that they seem quite lost without an author's words. No wonder Jesus said, Woe unto you hypocrites—play actors.

"IF YOU ARE GOING TO BE A PROTESTANT, WHY NOT 'BE' A PROT-estant?" I put this question again and again, to both myself and others. There is a great deal of disguised Roman Catholicism within our Protestant churches. Perhaps there is a natural Roman Catholic in us all, and he is strongest in those of us who are most anti–Roman Catholic. Very few people who wear the Protestant badge, as it were, have the courage to be consistently and completely what they claim to be.

Take the business of hankering after authority. It came up last night when I was talking to Douglas Collins. We were discussing a well-known evangelist and comparing his success with the comparative failure of the churches. "What we need is more authority in putting the message across," said Douglas. Only a day or two earlier I had heard the same comment from the lips of a Presbyterian minister, who was comparing the erratic attendance of his flock with the faithful attendance of the Roman Catholics at Mass, and hankering, as it seemed to me, after the authority of the Roman Catholic priest. It may be true that people want to be told, that they will listen to a man who states unequivocally, "The Bible says," and who speaks with burning conviction, undamped by "ifs" and "buts" and tentative suggestions. But if a man is a Protestant minister, he must be a Protestant minister. For him there are no finalities, no absolutes. Everything, his idea of God, his interpretation of the Bible, his diagnosis of people's sins, stands daily under the judgment of God, is fluid to the touch of God's spirit. He must not even pretend for the sake of greater effectiveness as a preacher that things are more final than they are. The essence of Protestantism is the

44

willingness to be in uncertainty with God. We are not in a rigid, static universe, but in one that is dynamic and growing; the important thing is not to have correct information about God but to be susceptible to God's spirit, to be growingly aware of his pressures upon our life. It is to be in fellowship with One who has more light and truth to break forth from his Word than we have yet received or yet glimpsed. This means that our preaching, whether men like it that way or not, must avoid dogmatism and finality. It must be tentative, groping, suggestive. We must ask men to take us seriously, but not literally. As Protestants we are travelers, always on the road and rejoicing to be on the road, for there, as on the Emmaus Road, Christ reveals himself, not in absolute information, but in the burning heart. And as for the business of wanting authority over our people, there is no such authority. The authority we possess is the authority we share with Christ, the laying aside of power, wealth, prestige, to serve in poverty and love and humility. I do not think we Protestants have yet begun to explore the spiritual meaning of poverty, the poverty which is deeper and more radical than the renunciation of worldly goods, and which Paul meant when he said, "Ye know the grace of our Lord Jesus Christ, that, though he was rich, . . . he became poor, that ye through his poverty might be rich." The only authority we possess or can possess is the authority of the man who wants nothing for himself, who seeks only to be made available to God and to his fellows.

But this is only one side of the secret, unconscious hankering after Roman Catholicism. It comes out in many other ways. Jack Lauder was saying the other night that it was a shame that our churches were only open on one day a week, and he made quite an impassioned appeal that we should consider keeping the doors open daily for private prayer and meditation. Fine. But it is not only economic considerations, like the cost of heating and lighting and the caretaker's salary, that lie behind our unopened churches. As Protestants we believe that a man can pray wherever he is, at home, at work, or on top of a tramcar, and further that his work duly offered up to God is his prayer. For the Roman Catholic, no doubt, there is something especially effective about prayers offered within a sacred building through the specially appointed channels. It comes out again in the oft-reiterated statement that our Protestant young people are much less aware of their faith than their Roman Catholic companions and consequently less able to talk about what they believe or to argue with the pagan or the communist. This may or may not be true. I have yet to meet these so well-instructed Roman Catholic young people I hear so much about. But even if it was true that they exist in great numbers, it would prove nothing. The fact is that our young people never can be as well instructed in the faith as the Roman Catholics are reputed to be. For the Protestant, faith is not merely intellectual apprehension of a doctrinal position; it is, as Luther pointed out, a living relationship to Jesus Christ, and this cannot be formulated with the exactitude and finality of a creed. Knowing a catechism is one thing; knowing Christ in his living, renewing, and saving power is another. By all means let us teach our young people to defend the faith, but the more important thing is to know what it is by experience.

ONE OF THE MOST DIFFICULT REQUESTS I GET AS A PASTOR IS TO recommend a good, simple book on the Christian faith for the ordinary layman. Time and time again I have had books returned with the comment, "I'm afraid that was too deep for me, Padre." I think a lot of this is sheer laziness on the part of the man in the pew. He wants to curl up with a good book; without any expenditure of effort on his part he wants to be admitted into the secrets of the universe! But religious writers must share some of the blame too. It is a striking fact that the most successful popular expositors of the faith are not clergymen. I have lent out a collection of published wireless talks on "Why I Believe." The contributors are distinguished theologians and preachers in the main, but the chapter that excites most comment and proves most helpful to ordinary people is one written by a young Scottish actor, Tom Fleming. And it is not because C. S. Lewis is a professor of English literature, but I suspect because he is a layman, that his work is so readily understood by the laity. It is not a question of style or literary ability; it is a question of attitude. It boils down to a difference in approach. Some time ago I shared in a student campaign in a small town. We were paired off; a minister and a student were given a joint assignment. The minister preached, and the student gave his testimony to what Christ had done for him. I assumed this would be the pattern as usual, but when we got to the church, young Bob said, "Let me preach the sermon tonight, and you tell the congregation what Christ means to you." He pulled me up with a jerk. Is that the trouble with us ministers, that we are preaching sermons and not sharing with people our living, up-to-date experience of God in Christ?

-------- *18* --------

CONRAD NOEL, THE VICAR OF THAXTED, ONCE SAID THAT TO improve the appearance of a church it was necessary only to take something out of it. His own lovely church, when he became its incumbent, was cluttered up with fussy ecclesiastical furniture, too many ornaments, vases, boxes, chairs, and occasional tables; by making a clean sweep of them he let the noble proportions of the building speak for themselves. Space and light have more to do with the beauty of a sanctuary than decoration that is merely stuck on.

We could improve more than the church *building* by taking things out! Many people, especially of the younger sort, would be attracted to Christianity were they able to see the strong pillars of the faith undistracted by the messy muddle of secondary beliefs, denominational tradition, local usage and custom. At present they cannot see the beauty of holiness for the squalor and triviality associated with it; we have placed the laws of God and the bylaws of man on the same level, and the result is not inviting. Studdert-Kennedy used to say that for the man in the street religion was a curious amalgam of mothers' meetings, Jonah and the whale, and the Archbishop of Canterbury's 7,500 pounds a year. Perhaps the man in the pew is equally confused when he hears his pastor and teachers arguing so vehemently about modes of baptism, church order, ecclesiastical procedure, equating the social habits of a particular class with the ethics of Jesus, paying more attention to these peripheral matters than to the weighty demands for love and charity, insisting as much, if not more, upon the correct forms of doctrine than upon the living experience that once called the doctrine forth. I have occasionally said to worried young seekers, "Believe as little as you can! Believe only what is inevitable!" Only that which forces itself upon our attention, only that which cannot be denied, however much we try to deny it, is worthy of our serious attention. Too many lives are cluttered up with a multitude of opinions, ideas, problems, which have a purely local or expedient interest. Emerson was surely right when he said to the young bloods of his day, "Resist much! Say 'No' as often as you say 'Yes'!" In the same spirit I often advise young people to look steadily at the life of Jesus and the experience of the early Church. "Let it speak candidly to your life and to your need, and give your wholehearted assent only to that which, reason as you will, you cannot in all honesty deny."

All this comes to my mind because earlier this evening Kenneth Cole, hesitating on the doorstep to the ministry, was in my study airing his doubts and indecisions, questioning the wisdom of offering his life service to an institution so fragmentarily divided, so rent with denominational loyalties. Frankly I could hold out no hope that such a squalid state of affairs is on the eve of passing away. If anything, our little denominational differences seem to loom larger every year; more and more "reasons" are found for our continued separation. I incline to think that no progress will be made as long as we concentrate on the subject of unity. The problem will never be solved; it might, however, disappear as many other insoluble problems have done in the past by becoming irrelevant. Our internal differences as denominations may one day cease to be interesting, may in fact become boring, in face of some real problem that we have allowed to engage our attention.

I am not a prophet, but I would like to think that that new and all-absorbing problem might come as we attend to the voices that are speaking to us from the East. In Rabindranath Tagore's *Letters to a Friend* he confides to C. F. Andrews: "The most important of all facts in the present age is that East and West have met. So long as it remains a mere fact, it will give rise to interminable conflicts, it will hurt even a man's soul. It is the mission of all men to raise this fact into a truth." That was written in 1920, and events meantime have only served to underline it. We are confronted today with two alternatives: lofty isolation from the other great faiths—Hinduism, Buddhism, Islam—leaving religion divided and too weak to resist the onslaught of secular forces, or a concerted effort of all faiths. We have too long been content, not merely to ignore one another's existence, but even to acquiesce in misrepresenting one another, instead of boldly grasping the hand of men of the stature of Tagore and S. Radhakrishnan for common understanding and co-operation. If we attempted this, the differences among such closely related groups as Methodists, Baptists, Anglicans, Presbyterians, and Congregationalists would surely assume their proper proportions.

And what has Christianity to fear from such an approach? Rudolf Otto, the Marburg theologian, surely spoke the true Christian word when he said, "No religion should die until its last and deepest word has been spoken." Is not that our task as Christians in the twentieth century, to apply the words of Jesus, "I am not come to destroy but to fulfil," not merely to the religion of the Old Testament, but to the living religions of the world? This is a very different attitude from eclecticism, the merging of the faiths or finding some mythical common denominator. It means the positive and friendly effort to understand and appreciate and welcome and work with all that is good within the religions of mankind, in the name of and in utter loyalty to Jesus Christ.

19

THE BEST THING ABOUT MY SERMON TO THE THEOLOGICAL students at the opening of the new session was the text. I chose the wise words of Eccl. 2:1, "My son, if thou comest to serve the Lord, prepare thy soul for temptation." Some of the earnest young men who have given up jobs in offices (most of our new recruits come from the white-collar class) fondly imagine that during their stay in a theological college they will be leading a comparatively sheltered life, surrounded by incentives to holiness and selfless service. Certainly they will be spared the monotonous and meaningless bad language of the factory and the office; they will not be chaffed or subtly persecuted for not joining in the weekly "raffle" or getting tight on the firm's outing. But a student's life, even a theological student's life, has its own peculiar temptations. One is the temptation to accept its privileges as a right. Another is to regard oneself as in some way "superior" to the young worker or young businessman. It is well to remind yourself, I said, that the life of leisure for study is a gift presented to you by society. I stressed this point because I have seen many a tragedy resulting from its ignorance. And perhaps the greatest tragedy is isolation, the creation of a special class, a thin rootless intelligentsia, unable to communicate with ordinary people.

I must say that these would-be parsons listened to me quite patiently as I tried to be honest from within my own experience and to share with them some of the temptations that assail people like myself. Of course we share the normal temptations of other human beings, but we have a few of our own special ones thrown in for good measure! One is the temptation to imagine that we have *done* something because we have *said* something, that we have found a solution when in fact we have only coined a phrase. We are professional talkers, as much at the mercy of words as words are at our mercy. We shall be tempted into imagining that because we have urged men to repent, we ourselves have repented; that because we urge the claims of Christ, we ourselves have met them; that because we talk about sacrifice, we ourselves have made sacrifices.

I said more, and when I got home, I took out this journal and applied it to myself. What are my special temptations as a minister? They are so many that I can only list them under the briefest headings.

1. To be approved by my congregation, to be liked by everybody.

2. To fulminate against sins that no one in the congregation is in the least interested in committing.

3. To be bold in theological thinking, but tame and conventional in social and ethical thinking. People will put up with, and even enjoy, theological heresy, but they prefer the man in the pulpit to be orthodox in his political and social views.

4. To water down the austere demands of the gospel, not so

much from fear, as out of sympathy with men and women whose difficulties I appreciate only too well.

5. To spend time with people I like and who obviously like me.
6. To choose subjects for sermons and addresses that fit my mind rather than stretch it.
7. To trade on my natural gifts instead of allowing God to work in me and through me.

These may not sound like very terrible temptations to the man in the street, and he may wonder what all the fuss is about. But in fact, whether in the world or in the church, whether through the flesh or through the mind, all temptation is the same—it is the refusal of the challenge to be great, not simply good or harmless or respectable, but to be great; it is the acceptance of the second-best; it is telling God, in effect, that I don't want to be fully and responsibly human.

20

THE FIRST BOOK I EVER BOUGHT WITH MY OWN MONEY WAS *The Collected Poems of John Masefield*. I look at its pale blue cover and remember nostalgically the studious boy in the Norfolk jacket and short trousers marching into the town bookseller's clutching a ten shilling note. How he got hold of the note I do not remember, for he was still at school and pocket money in those days was limited to sixpence a week. I rather fancy it was a gift from a Socialist uncle, himself a great reader—of Blatchford, Jack London, and Winwood Reade, of course. Neither can I remember now what had brought Masefield to the boy's attention, for he had never heard of book reviews. But I can savor yet the excitement of owning and carrying off that bulky volume, the thrill of reading *The Everlasting Mercy,* a thrill made more delicious because, though a religious poem, it contained so much bad langauge. "I'll bloody him a bloody fix"—how that rolled off the tongue!

In one's early teens poetry has to be religious, didactic, and melancholy—especially melancholy. How often with Shelley I fell upon the thorns of life, I bled. With Keats I ceased upon the midnight with no pain. But with the inconsistency of youth I was also up and doing with Samuel Smiles. And then there followed a dreamy period when I devoured the novels of W. J. Locke, of which I do not now remember a single word. I bought every book of A. C. Benson's and considered him the greatest English essayist, though why the sedative musings of an elderly don should appeal to a schoolboy in shorts baffles me.

But the first book that rearranged the furniture of my mind, that started me thinking, as the saying goes, was Jack London's *Martin Eden.* It was the autobiographical element in this novel that attracted me; I was not, and never have been, a Jack London fan, his tales of adventure left me cold, but I sensed from *Martin Eden* the possibility of adventures of the mind. I became conscious that here was a world of ideas, and inevitably of course I became a Socialist. From this novel I became aware of names like Karl Marx, Nietzsche, Herbert Spencer, whose unreadable works I borrowed from the library and carried under my arm ostentatiously. How I fitted my youthful Christianity into all this, I cannot now recall, but fit it in I did, for the figure and personality of Jesus held me then as it holds me now. I rather suspect that I saw Jesus in a workman's jacket as the first real Socialist, as the Superman beyond good and evil, as the crown of the evolutionary process. Curiously enough, though Jack London was a fierce critic of institutional Christianity, his strictures on the church passed me by. The church he knew might have in it timid, time-serving, obscurantist bishops and capitalist vestry-men who ground the faces of the poor, but that was something in a book. The church I knew was a back-street Bethel, where all the deacons were workingmen, which was my home. I, too, was a critic of institutional Christianity in theory; in practice I was deeply and gratefully involved in its life.

No book read in later life has the same stunning impact as the book read in the *Sturm und Drang* of adolescence. But I am grateful that I am still young enough in spirit at any rate to be influenced by the written word. In the last two decades I think that the books that have influenced me most are Ortega y Gasset's *The Revolt of the Masses,* Lawrence Hyde's *The Learned Knife,* and quite recently Nels Ferré's *The Christian Understanding of God.* What I got from Ortega y Gasset was a fresh understanding of the times in which we live, from Hyde a new understanding of the qualifications for understanding, and from Ferré a new vision of the purpose and character of God. *The Revolt of the Masses* abounds in such sentences as these, which have now become the commonplaces of thought: "The mediocre mind, knowing itself to be mediocre, has the assurance to proclaim the rights of the mediocre and to impose them wherever it will." "Two fundamental traits of the mass man of today—the free expansion of his vital desires, and therefore of his personality; and his radical ingratitude towards all that has made possible his easy existence." In *The Learned Knife,* Lawrence Hyde cuts away the pretensions of "scientific" observers by the application of scientific method and keen intelligence to arrive at truth. In the end, he says, "they are ingenious attempts to get something for nothing." "You cannot, merely by being very, very scrupulous and painstaking, find out what other people have discovered by passion, sacrifice, faith and suffering." "It is only the regenerated man who can achieve a vision of organic society." From Nels Ferré I have learned to see that "being is becoming," that love is the nature of being-becoming, and that God's revelation in Jesus through incarnation was an open and creative, not a closed or final, truth.

21

WHY ARE CHRISTIAN PEOPLE SO "GOOD"? SOMETIMES I GET THE impression that their God inhabits a large and drafty church, that serving him consists in sitting in hard pews, the harder the more virtuous; that for them God's jurisdiction ends at the church door. I took the chair this afternoon at a United Prayer Meeting, at which that lovely man Professor Carr gave a fine, scholarly exposition of the work of the Holy Spirit. Wouldn't it be fun, I thought, as I trudged through the snow, if old Carr broke loose and told us all to look for and rejoice in the Holy Spirit in the swirl of ballet skirts, in the ecstasy of young love, in the swing of dumbbells, in the panting and heaving of a Rugby scrum? Why must we always think of the spiritual in terms of model behavior? Is it not the restless Spirit of God that urges us to create and conquer, to conquer not only sin, but all untamed territories of the mind? Is he not active wherever there are movement, music, color? In the rise of the sap, the tensed muscles of a spear of grass, in wrestling with a mathematical problem, in introducing order into accounts, in creating a home? But, instead, dear old Carr treated us to a careful, balanced survey of the subject, from which all the rich juices had been extracted, and we came out feeling vaguely uplifted when we should have come out raging mad to create in co-operation with the Creator, to wrestle with all the dumb, intractable, stubborn, formless stuff of our daily experience.

22

BARRIE ANDREWS MOTORED ME OUT TO SELKIRK TODAY. A GLOrious spring day and the drive from Edinburgh was perfect. Barrie is a delightful host, a lovely combination of ardent churchman and lover of the arts, by profession a salesman but possessed of a ranging mind and a willingness to discuss any idea under heaven. We talked and talked on the way and had a splendid lunch at the Ettrick Shaw Hotel, then walked over to Ettrick Church and called at the manse for the key. After inspecting the Auld Kirk, with its double-decker pulpit, box pews, and longhandled offertory boxes, we strolled round the graveyard, burial place of Thomas Boston of *The Fourfold State* and Will O'Phaup, "distinguished for feats of frolic, agility and strength," and of course of the Ettrick Shepherd, James Hogg.

When we returned the key to the manse, we were invited in by the lady of the house to take tea and to meet her husband, Dr. Addison, the parish "meeneester." It was like living in another age. Dr. Addison as a result of diabetes and an accident is growing blind and went over with us the outline of the sermon he proposes to preach next Sunday, his last sermon in the parish after twenty-four years. He never once referred to the church as the "church," but as the "shrine." He bemoaned the new-fashioned ways and regarded it as a tragedy that the children of the parish were forced to go into the neighboring town for their schooling. He evidently regarded Selkirk as a dangerous place! And then as a parting act he presented us with a printed card, a rhymed paraphrase of the creed which he had prepared for the boys and girls of his parish. Whatever else he had done or not done, he suggested, he had left this permanent memorial of his pastoral love. Barrie and I felt humbled by this fleeting contact with a choice spirit, a real man of God.

23

I CALLED TODAY ON DICK MORRIS, A SIXTY-YEAR-OLD TRAVELER for a paper manufacturer, a fine, friendly man, a member of my church, who has been ill for some weeks with vague pains and general depression. It was a good sign, I thought, when he began to talk about his loss of confidence in himself, his reluctance to go back on the road, because I am sure it is his mind and not his body that is sick. I have lately been absorbed in Paul Tillich's weighty little book *The Courage to Be,* a book written by a philosophical theologian which has given me more insight into the human situation than any psychology I have ever read. What I have gained from his book is the knowledge that man, not neurotic man, but every man simply because he is a man, faces three threats to his existence: the threat of guilt, the threat of death, and the threat of meaninglessness. And I suppose that these three threats reach their greatest intensity when a man has passed the fifty mark. As I am just coming up to this mark myself, I speak feelingly! Death is certainly more than an academic subject nowadays. I have become self-conscious about my age, and this is associated with a dread of loss of potency, not in the physical sense, but in the sense of losing one's grip, one's power to hold and interest people, to retain the affections of people and to gain new friends. I suspect that few men reach the age of fifty without questioning the meaning of life and of their own lives in particular.

> O God!
> How weary, stale, flat, and unprofitable
> Seem to me all the uses of this world,

cried Hamlet, but then he was a prince with plenty of time on his hands, not a minister with an absorbing job and many interests and people dependent upon him. But one day last week, visiting in a pleasant suburb, I suddenly stopped dead in my tracks and asked myself, "What the deuce am I doing here?" It was a frightening feeling, for "here" did not simply mean this characterless, standardized suburban road, but anywhere. The decent villas and trim hedges leered at me, as if to question my existence. That mood soon passed, but I didn't like it while it lasted!

So I am not surprised that Dick Morris has taken to his bed.

A man has to have deep inner resources and faith in something more profound than his business, hobbies, and home if he is to meet the existential threats that Tillich so clearly describes. I talked to Dick about this, but with a feeling that he wasn't listening and that he was incapable of listening.

Later

Since I wrote the above, months have passed, and Dick has changed his doctor, has submitted to many physical examinations, for the symptoms change from month to month, and has been in the care of a psychologist, but gets no better.

Later still

Mrs. Morris, alarmed and desperate, brought in yet another psychologist, who took Dick into his private nursing home and has been treating him with shock therapy or some equivalent of it. The result is almost miraculous. After two weeks Dick is nearly back to his old self. I suppose that what has happened is that his whole system has been toned up so as to grapple more strongly with his own problem. In the end, I think, no one can do anything for a man who is suffering from lack of confidence in himself except strengthen him to bear and to face and so to overcome his weakness. It seems to have been done in this case with a minimum of talk simply by the application of a physical method, but I do not believe that is the whole story. The physical toning-up without Dick's general background of Christianity, his lifelong membership in the church, and his faith in and understanding of Christ, however rudimentary, would have been powerless to effect a cure. But the physical means used has certainly speeded up the process of self-recovery.

24

LEADING A CONGREGATION IN PRAYER IS THE MOST DIFFICULT part of my public work. I spend a great deal of my time, though less than I should, on preparing prayers or leads for prayer, and sometimes I envy people like my neighbor Leslie Houseman, who with no preliminary preparation just stands up in the pulpit, opens his little blue-and-gold book at the appropriate page, and starts reading out what is set down—beautiful, impeccably theological prayers, all in the right liturgical order. What strain and tension he is spared! And he can never make an absolute hash of things. But no, it is not true that I envy him. In my heart I know that it is the greatest privilege in the world to try to gather up in concrete terms the thanksgiving, longings, hopes, of a congregation one loves and has grown to know through the years.

Not long ago I attended a conference on the better ordering of church services. We discussed the question of free versus liturgical prayers, and the argument was all in favor of the book, with its wide sweep, oneness with the Church universal, beauty of language, deliverance from the minister's moods, and so forth. I went on from that conference to a meeting at Livingstone House. I don't remember what the meeting was about, but I shall never forget the man who led the opening devotions. Howard was a big, bluff, rather slangy man, but that day he prayed with such pastoral particularity, such profound understanding of ordinary people caught up in the problems of modern life, showed such sympathy with men and women harassed by worry, stung into irritation, and driven through frustration into self-mutilation, that the hearts of all present were strangely warmed. No prayers from a book, I thought and still think, can compare with the free prayer of a man with a real pastoral heart.

When I think of my own public prayers, I see that the least satisfactory part of them is the attempt to gather up the confessions of the people. The thanksgiving and petitions are easy enough, but when it comes to "Lead us not into temptation" and I try to break that down into minute particulars, I realize that the occasions of temptation for minister and people are miles apart, and I have to think very hard indeed to envisage myself facing the temptations of sharp practice in business, of indulging in gambling or drinking for the sake of fellowship with one's work mates. This is where Howard scored; he knew his people as few men in the ministry know them. He was the sort of man they trusted and found it easy to talk to. There was no trace of professionalism about him, no suspicion that he was more interested in maintaining a code than in serving and loving them.

25

I PUT DOWN KAREN HORNEY'S BOOK "SELF-ANALYSIS" AND BEGAN to ruminate on my relationship with my father. He has been dead for twenty years. I think it is twenty, but I cannot be sure. I try hard to recall any memorable conversation, any kind of intimacy, and I cannot. It is with the greatest effort that I summon up what he looked like. I seem deliberately to have pushed his memory into the background, though "pushed" is a strong word; it would be truer to say that his memory has just faded away. As far as I can tell, he had no influence on me. I remember him saying that he, too, used to read books when he was a youngster, but the desire for sustained reading had left him by the time he married. His reading at home consisted of the daily paper, *The News of the World* on Sunday, and the old green-covered *Tit-Bits*. He was not a religious man, though he went to church fairly regularly. But I wonder. Was he more religious than I suspected? Suddenly there comes back an image of him singing hymns with great gusto at a Sunday evening service. But then he was half Welsh, half Cornish.

(I wonder why I am thinking of him now after twenty years of almost complete black-out. Perhaps it has something to do with the arrival of my own middle age. Maybe it is because I have arrived at the age at which he left us. And perhaps there is another reason. Young Evans was in the other night, complaining of his sense of isolation at home and particularly of his inability to make contact with his father. He seemed to imagine that he was unique in this—that other young fellows had a warm, intimate, companionable relationship with their fathers and that he was the exception. And I had been trying to tell him that it was not so. This father-son relationship that he thinks normal— the easy comradeship, the interchange of experiences, the sharing of problems and secrets—is the rarest thing in the world, and perhaps it is better so. Maybe Nature herself had put that barrier there, guarding us against the misuse or exploitation of intimate knowledge by people with whom we have to live in close physical contact day in and day out. That is why many young people find it easier to make a confidant of an older person outside the imme-diate family circle.)

But to get back to father. He had a reputation for being a

competent and painstaking workman. He had his own little business, but though he loved his work, he hated presenting bills. It was my mother or one of us children who had to go round collecting debts. I supposed he liked people's approval too much to bother them for money. He was easygoing in most ways, easily touched for a loan, and I suppose this is something I have inherited from him—the desire to be regarded as a good fellow. But there is one way in which I do not resemble him: he was a confirmed gambler, especially fond of playing cards until the early hours of the morning with his three brothers and friends. But he gambled on horses, too, and this, I remember vividly, caused more unpleasantness at home than anything else. This probably accounts for the fact that I have never gambled in my life, not even a bob on the Derby, and why I regard card playing as a shocking waste of time.

But his relationship with me, his eldest son? Well, I can hardly remember anything about it. We had no interests in common. I had no aptitude for mechanical work and no desire to follow him into the business. I don't remember that we ever discussed it or that he even hinted at it. With my two brothers it was a foregone conclusion, but I was the "clever one" of the family! So in due time I sat the scholarship examination for the Grammar School, and he concurred in this, but left my mother to work out the ways and means. Again, when I entered the theological college, he said nothing, but was, I gathered from others, proud that his eldest boy was going to be a minister.

As the years passed, we treated each other rather like casual friends; he never attempted to give me any advice, or to interfere with my decisions, or to inquire into my plans, still less to share them. And I ask myself, Is my experience normal or abnormal? And was I more to blame than he, since I was the articulate one?

And linking up with Karen Horney, how far am I deficient or lopsided as a personality because of this rather tenuous and unsatisfactory relationship?

26

SO MANY PEOPLE I MEET IN THESE DAYS ARE OBVIOUSLY WANTING to punish themselves. They are trying to work out their own salvation by being their own Christs. They scorn the thought of Christ dying for them, and so they are putting themselves to death by inches. When a man refuses God's mercy, he can do nothing but hate himself.

Just before midnight there was a cautious tap at the window. It was John Ireland, a lad in his early twenties who is making an awful hash of his university course. He was half drunk, had been walking about town, unable to sit still in his digs, unable to concentrate on reading, though he has an examination tomorrow. "I'm a failure, a complete flop," he said. "The clever boy who didn't make good." And so he went on torturing himself, probing the exposed nerve. And then he began to talk about conquering his passions. This made me really angry. "No, not conquering them, but using them creatively! Why all this talk about conquering, damping down, holding in check? Why not let yourself go?" Tipsy as he was, I think he was really shocked at me for this. You see, he had come round to me, not for sympathy or advice, but for yet another hiding. He wanted me to apply the whip, to bully him, to humiliate him, and I refused to play his little game. "You've punished yourself enough already," I said. "But you'll get precious little satisfaction out of that." When I began to talk about Christ, he burst out, "Christ can't do anything for me; I won't let him." "No, just as you won't let your friends love you. You are too proud to accept love and friendship free; you must pay for it. What are you trying to prove, Johnnie? Forget all about your sins! Why, you haven't got any sins worth mentioning. There's only one real sin, Johnnie, and that's the refusal to accept grace, the refusal to let your friends love you, the refusal to believe that God loves you, not because you are you, but because he is God."

He got away about 1 A.M. soberer than when he came and still suspicious of me, still disappointed that I had not given him the dressing down that he knew he deserved—and wanted. When he had gone, I said my prayers and searched my own heart. I am not likely to get drunk; I don't like the stuff! But I wonder how much of the work I drive myself to do, the good deeds I do, are my attempt to atone for my own sins. "Lord," I pray, "I believe in the forgiveness of sins—my sins; help thou mine unbelief."

----------- *27* -----------

I WONDER WHETHER WE PREACHERS PAY ENOUGH ATTENTION TO boredom. We are alleged to be experts at inflicting it! But if we preached on it oftener, we might help to dissipate some of it. More people commit sins because they are bored than because they are daring, rebellious sinners. Gabriel Marcel speaks of the

tedium vitae, the boredom and disgust with living, which claims as its victims hundreds of thousands of human beings who do not even know how to recognize the disease which is attacking them; we must not forget that many of the most incurable ailments to which man is subject are painless and not easy to detect for a long time.

The short answer that many of us could give for our private self-indulgences, our reckless infliction of pain on others, and our outbursts of malicious gossip is "I was bored."

But behind boredom lies something of which it is but a symptom, namely, self-despair. It is when we have but a poor conceit of ourselves that we fall into sins, that we give way to the flesh. It seems that in such moments we want to humiliate ourselves still further. That is why I regard it as part of my pastoral ministry to bolster up the self-esteem of my young people. According to one of my deacons "they need taking down a peg or two, having the conceit knocked out of them." So it seems on the surface. But if he had shared their confidence as I have done, he would realize that some of them, the ones who appear most confident and overbearing and cocky, are in reality a quivering mass of self-doubt, self-disgust, self-despair.

When I worked in the slums, it was very noticeable that the boys who got into trouble with the police were almost all youngsters in "dead-end jobs," people with no skill or opportunity to affirm themselves in their work. The lads who were learning a trade and were thus proving themselves, gaining each day in self-esteem, kept out of trouble. It is fashionable now to attribute juvenile delinquency to "broken homes," but my experience inclines me to think that most crime is committed by people who have nothing to sell the community, no good opinion of themselves.

But it is an exhausting job, this business of being an "encourager." Some people seem determined to think ill of themselves. To tell them that God loves them is only a phrase until one has helped them to probe the depths of their own self-hatred.

28

MOST SERMONS ARE PREACHED ON THE ASSUMPTION THAT MEN want to know the truth, that they are inwardly tormented, puzzled by the mysteries of life. But the great mass of men are not remotely interested in truth; they do not mind a bit of an argument, and for the sake of a good discussion they can produce a few "puzzlers." But they are usually religious puzzles rather than human ones. They see the difficulties of Christian doctrine and ignore the difficulties of their own everyday lives. They find it difficult to believe in miracles, but they do not question the miracle of their own existence. They cannot accept the fact that Christ is both God and man, but they accept the fact of their own inward divisions. They ask, What's the use of going to church? but very rarely, What's the use of living? That seems to them self-evident.

Is not that why many sermons do not reach the people to whom they are preached? We are giving the answers to questions nobody is asking. We are providing solutions to difficulties that have hardly been felt. The preacher's first job is to provoke the questions, to make men aware of the strangeness of the human situation they take for granted.

Years ago T. E. Hulme pointed out in his brilliant book *Speculations* that there are certain ideas so widely accepted that they have attained the status of categories. "We do not see them, but see other things through them." Would it not be profitable for preachers to examine these assumptions upon which people live, the unconscious and undetected attitudes they take up to life? Instead of starting with some remote ideal, let us take men where they are, earning a living, building a home, sacrificing for their children, keeping up appearances. What is the meaning of all this mass of activity? And there are other assumptions to which we can profitably put a question mark. That men have a right to be happy; that unhappiness is exceptional and unfair; that every man has a right to his own opinion; that science is the only road to truth; that religious faith is necessarily blind and superstitious; that if God does indeed exist, his chief function is to further man's happiness.

As a matter of fact most men are living on assumptions nobler and better than their conscious creeds. There are hidden Christian assumptions behind their everyday actions. It is part of the preacher's task, and a more profitable part than merely nagging them, to unearth and reveal these assumptions. As I once heard a wise teacher say, "Remember that religious experience is not a strange and uncanny sort of experience; it is normal experience understood at full depth."

29

One of the most moving pieces of writing I know is found at the end of *Ego 9,* the last volume of James Agate's diary. Agate was not superficially a religious man; his loves were the theater, horses, conversation, food and drink, and good cigars. But five days before he died at the age of sixty-nine, he wrote:

I thank Thee, God, for all the things life has meant to me. For the seaside and cricket on the sands which made up my childhood. For the golf courses and show-yards of my youth and middle-age. For the books, acting, and music, recollections of which make my old age rich and enviable. For the stone walls of Derbyshire, the dales of Yorkshire, Welsh mountains, and English lakes. For fun, good talk, and enjoyment of the mind of others. For brother Edward's wit and courage. For brother Harry, who has taught me what unselfishness may be. For Leo Pavia. For those great spirits—Montague, Monkhouse, Mair. For the loyalty and devotion of my friends everywhere. For the humble friends and helpers who have made my work possible. For any talent I may have possessed, and the gift of energy to prosecute it. For never having utterly lost the sense of the glory and the freshness of a dream. For never having for one instant believed that there hath pass'd away a glory from the earth. For the power of being two persons.

> I loved the garish day, and, spite of fears,
> Pride ruled my will: remember not past years.

It does me good simply to copy that out. When a man can express his gratitude like that, it does not surprise me that he is an attractive man. There are little men who cannot give tongue to their appreciation, not because they have not the gift of words, but because they have no gift for gratitude; they want to claim all the credit for themselves, they think it a weakness to confess indebtedness to others. I suppose it takes a big man to shout his dependence on others from the housetops. An American friend recently sent me a copy of the *Saturday Review* for 2nd October, 1954, which contains an article by Arnold Toynbee, "I Owe My Thanks," in which he pays tribute to his benefactors: to Marcus Aurelius for teaching him to return thanks to his benefactors; to his mother for making him a historian; to Edward Gibbon for showing him by example what a historian could do; to people, institutions, landscapes, monuments, pictures, languages, and books for exciting his curiosity; to people and books for teaching him methods of intellectual work; to people and books for teaching him methods of literary presentation; to people, monuments, apparatus, pictures, books, and events for giving him intuitions and ideas; to people and institutions for showing kindness to him. For page after page Toynbee goes on pouring out his gratitude, until one's own heart takes fire.

I would like to be capable of writing with such gusto and such obvious delight. I would know that I was a religious man in very truth if, without stopping to think or weigh or balance, I could let my pen go in sentences of praise. But I am a reluctant praiser; I have to scratch my head and think. For what could I thank God most sincerely? I almost tremble to begin the list, lest the catalogue should give me away, should reveal how narrow my heart is, how self-centered and full of little pride my heart is. I draw a sheet of paper toward me, feeling nervous lest I should fail in this test. I will put nothing down, I say, that does not come instinctively, spontaneously.

"I thank thee, God, for health . . . and I remember how grossly I have misused and taken advantage of my body, depending thoughtlessly on days of painless health. . . . I thank thee, God, for parents who, though they saw me grow away from them, intellectually and spiritually, and found no tongue to share their thoughts, welcomed me, shared their home with me, loved me; for friends, mentally and spiritually towering above me, who were not cruel enough to deflate my pretentiousness or to expose my thin veneer of learning, but encouraged me to develop, who listened patiently to half-baked ideas and secondhand opinions until some small shoots of sincerity and originality made their way to the surface; for the Church of Jesus Christ, holding me in childhood, adolescence, and young manhood; for the little companies of working men and women, some of them 'far ben' in holy things, who treated me as a son when I was younger and as a spiritual father when I was older; for my wife, for pretending not to notice my selfishness, my arrogance of spirit, my cool way of throwing responsibility upon her; for children who have allowed me to be their friend; for young men and women who have honored me with their confidence; for friends of my own age who have encouraged me to use what gifts I have, bullying me into print and speech; for the books that surround me, fortifying my spirit, giving words to formless thoughts and stretching a mind naturally narrow and timid; above all, for the poets, for Keats and Shelley, for enabling me to bear the weight of my lumpish adolescence; for Wordsworth, Shakespeare, for disclosing the power of the word; for Blake for teaching me true spirituality; for the moderns, especially Eliot and Auden, for revealing the world to me, not the world of nature, but the pressing world of ideas, assumptions, institutions. . . ." And so I could go on. But I have left something out that I am reluctant to put down in black and white, my indebtedness to Jesus Christ. How often I have hesitated in the public prayer of thanksgiving, after listing the temporal mercies and the gifts of providence, before going on to utter the formula, "But most of all, we thank thee for Jesus Christ. . . ." When I try to spell that formula out in living speech, I am afraid to say too much, afraid to say too little. What, in fact, does Jesus Christ mean to me? Stripped of all pious verbiage and conventional phraseology, what can I honestly say? He is the shaper of the world in which I live. It is a different world because he once lived within it. Its very architecture, its institutions, its manners, are what they are, imperfect though they be, because he existed, taught, healed, and blessed. My mental, my private, world is haunted by him. Everything I think and do and say must sooner or later meet the scrutiny of his eyes; it is either approvable or condemnable by him. He is the molder of the thoughts, ideas, and speech of my best friends; it would be impossible to imagine them without his influence upon them. He is the enemy of all that is base, dirty, and mean in my most intimate privacy. He humanizes my thought of God. He puts compassion into my relationships with others. He sets my life in a context that would be utterly different without him, for it would not include the Church, and his Church is the biggest single factor in my life. Without it I could not imagine myself.

All this, I suspect, is most inadequate theologically. I do not find it easy to sing, "Christ died for me." I can easily believe that he died because of me.

30

WE WERE DISCUSSING WIRELESS PROGRAMS. NEARLY ALL THE youngsters in the Youth Club listen in to either Radio Luxumbourg or the Light Program. They rarely select their listening—unless there is a big fight on! They are aware that there is something called "The Home Service," and they associate it with everything that is suburban, smug, and cozy, though they tolerate it for it obviously meets a need among older people. But when it comes to the Third Program, the case is different. They do not merely dislike it, they resent it. Indeed, I do not think it too much to say that they hate it—not the material that is put across, which they have never heard, but the very thought of it. They feel that someone is in conspiracy against them, trying to put one across on them. But then it is not only the young bloods who sense the patronage and condescension of the Third. I have observed this suspicion and dislike of "high-brows" in more mature circles within the Church. We talk about class divisions, but this goes deeper than class, and it cuts across class divisions. The workingman and the boss, the rich and the poor, are strangely at one when faced with modern art, modern poetry, modern music. They are uneasy in their presence; they feel, as Jimmy Cole said last night, that someone is pulling their legs, asserting a superiority of discernment and appreciation that is phony or just swank.

It requires a lot of moral courage to be a high-brow in the average church. Christian democracy requires that one should listen patiently, should avoid stressing things that isolate one from one's fellow men, and this so easily leads to acquiescence in general mediocrity. As Bernard Meland has said in *Seeds of Redemption,*

The most damnable thing the enlightened and sensitive mind can say about the Christian church is that it is mediocre. Its music is mediocre. Its architecture is mediocre. Its prayers are mediocre. Its parish talk is mediocre. Its celebrations are mediocre. . . . Platitudes are more valued than insights; familiar shibboleths than a discerning word.

And this mediocrity is permitted because we have too moral a conception of the good life. Our people do not see the importance of æsthetic standards and literary taste. They apply Paul's word about having a right judgment in all things only to ethical behavior. "Goodness" is "being kind to granny and the cat," is having high standards of personal honesty, fair dealing, consideration for others. It is not a sin to pass by the world's masterpieces with indifference, without curiosity. It is not a sin to read shoddy prose, or wallow in sentimental music, or rest the eye on chocolate-box art. Only in one department of life—the moral—are standards high and exacting. Yet we talk glibly enough about Christ being the Lord of all life. Ought not a Christian to be searching for the first-rate in every department of experience? Is there not such a thing as Christian discrimination in the realm of reading, listening, seeing? A few years ago I fled with a sense of shame from the promenade at a seaside resort, feeling that the mock Tudor and Elizabethan houses on the front were architectural lies. The men and women who live in these houses, who take pride in owning them, are all, I am sure, highly moral, respectable, honest people, who go to church and would feel uncomfortable about telling a lie, and yet they are willing to live in a lie—in a building tortured out of all semblance to reality, brick and steel masquerading as stone and old oak beams. But when I expressed my sense of shame about these pretty little houses, as though I had been in contact with the powers of darkness, I was accused of being hysterical.

———— *31* ————

IN A LIFETIME OF READING I HAVE COLLECTED HUNDREDS OF accounts of religious conversions. When I retire from the active ministry, I would like to study them in more detail and make a classification according to psychological types. Most of the accounts I have read are conversions to the Roman Catholic Church (the Roman Catholics are more publicity-minded than the Protestants), and it seems to me on a rough inspection that they fall into two groups—one, wherein the pressures of life lead to a demand for intellectual certainty; and two, wherein the uncommitted, rootless, and shapeless spirit cries out for order, not simply intellectual order, but for a definite and well-defined place within a neat and tidy scheme.

Charles Scott-Moncrieff, the translator of Proust, was converted to the Roman Catholic faith at the age of twenty-six. He had been brought up in the Anglican Church and loved the services of Winchester Cathedral, but began during the First World War to feel that his place was not there.

Towards the end of June my hand was forced by one of the two R.C. sergeants in my Company, who came to ask me about opportunities for religion, and prefaced it by begging my pardon and asking if I was not a Roman Catholic. I could not explain to him then, so I simply said yes, and it was arranged that the Brigade Chaplain should come to us at the Château. . . . I suddenly found that I *was* a Roman Catholic.

All the hesitation of years was suddenly crystallized into a decision by the matter-of-fact assumption of that sergeant.

Another example of conversion to Roman Catholicism occurs in the autobiography of the Hungarian journalist Eugene Bagger, *The Heathen Are Wrong.* Writing of an evening in February, 1933, he says:

I had seen the light, but refused to follow it, for the road was uphill and too arduous for one of my easy habits; and I said to myself that evening, not knowing that I was quoting Saint Augustine, "There is yet time." It is the one passage in the Confessions that all the world knows by heart and cites *con amore.* There are, writes Father D'Arcy, the English philosopher, many doors whereby a man may enter the Catholic Church; but the Church herself prefers the door of the intellect to any other. Well, the door was being held open for me, in February, 1933, by Mr. Aldous Huxley, Professor Sigmund Freud, and a few other scholars and gentlemen of their agnostic kind, all working in shifts; and they would have been surprised, though perhaps not flattered, to know what effect their writings had on one particular reader. But though the door was open, and I liked the illumination within, I still hesitated, for I preferred, for everyday purposes, the vague comfort of the twilight outside. I was eventually pushed in by the lady who said that Puccini was as good a composer as Bach, because *she* thought so, and her opinion was as good as anybody else's; and what was I going to do about it? I did nothing about it, except that I stepped through that door and shut it gently; and found myself sheltered for ever from ladies, and others, who claimed for their *obiter dicta* on music, and on any other subject, the infallibility that the Pope only claims for himself when he speaks officially on points of Catholic doctrine.

Turning for a moment from these serious and strenuous souls, I recall hearing of a Chinaman whose name was Lo something-or-other. He was converted on hearing a Christian preacher read aloud the words "Lo, I am with you alway even unto the end of the world." And why not? At the heart of every conversion there is a longing to count personally, to feel that one is directly addressed by God. And are not many conversions of this inconsequential order? The immediate occasion may be a trifling word, which assumes its importance because the subject was ready to make some sort of decision.

Protestant conversions, unlike conversions to the Roman Catholic Church, do not usually hinge upon the search for intellectual security. Where security enters at all, it is moral rather than intellectual safety and stability that are sought. What is usually sought is salvation in the sense of salvage from waste—from waste of one's powers through excess or aimlessness. Hence the Protetant emphasis on being "saved to serve." But as I say, we Protestants are not good at advertising our converts or at utilizing them for propaganda purposes.

———— *32* ————

ONE DIFFERENCE BETWEEN YEATS AND AE WAS THAT GEORGE Russell loved nothing so much as to read a young poet's manuscript. The discovery and encouragement of new talent was not Yeats's strong point. He was much too wrapped up in his own work. When I was starting out in the ministry, I belonged to a fraternal in which the rest of us formed an audience for the most brilliant preacher in West London. It was a delight and an education to hear him talk about his method of preparing sermons or to share with him in the working out of next Sunday's sermon. But he never asked us about our sermons! Not far away from my first manse there lived an equally brilliant preacher, who, taking pity on a bachelor, often invited me to lunch with his family. After lunch in his beautifully untidy study (the most workmanlike study I have ever seen!) he plied me with questions about my work, asked eagerly how I tackled the problem of college youth, or begged me to share with him my alleged success with children. Whereas Jimmy told us, Bill always asked us. He took it for granted that we were experts in some field or another and sought to avail himself of our superior insights. Of course we had no superior insights, but the compliment did us good, and we obediently racked our brains and produced something bigger and better than we had hitherto thought ourselves capable of.

In one department, church drama, Bill was a pioneer; he had adapted several religious classics for stage presentation; he had written an excellent and useful manual on the subject, but he invariably treated me as the expert and himself as the toiling, puzzled beginner. He canvassed my views; he listened patiently to my account of our very amateur efforts. How bored he must have been by my jejune opinions, but if he was, he never showed signs of it, and I invariably left his house feeling better for having been in his company. And come to think of it, I don't think he was bored, because although the opinions so feebly expressed might have been stale and secondhand or uselessly immature, he was genuinely enjoying the sight of a young man struggling to think and express himself. Many times in later life I have conjured up the keen, responsive face of Bill, and it has saved me from telling people when I ought to be asking them, from giving advice when the young fellow in front of me was wanting encouragement to talk.

33

WE ARE TRYING TO MAKE MEN AWARE OF GOD WHEN THEY ARE not even aware of life. Despite the apparent success of recent large-scale evangelistic campaigns, I am more convinced than ever that the first step in lasting evangelism is not trying to recover a sense of the supernatural, but seeking to make men conscious and curious about the life they are already living. Most modern men are living on the smooth, shiny, unexamined surface of existence; they do not realize that they are touching reality at second and even third hand. A text that haunts me more and more is the psalmist's words "Out of the depths have I cried unto thee, O Lord." Until we can produce that cry, not out of surface wants but from deep, subterranean need, all our talk of God is likely to be useless. And that is what we are doing in our churches: we are answering questions that nobody is asking. That is what makes sermons boring. As P. T. Forsyth once said, to be an interesting preacher it is not necessary to be brilliant, it is only necessary to be real. And when we talk about God, in a vacuum as it were, we are being thoroughly unreal. Men are not interested in God until they are first interested in themselves. Men cannot cry to God until they become real and fully personal at some point of their lives. And so much of the apparatus of modern civilization is designed to keep us away from reality, is designed expressly to give us secondhand experience. We encounter time in the clock and not in the sun, we experience cold and heat through the thermometer, we touch society through organization, and so on.

I do not know who John Wren-Lewis is except that he is a layman, but his article in the *Hibbert Journal* (October, 1954) contains the best sense on evangelism that I have read in many a day. He makes the shatteringly obvious point, which we nevertheless keep on ignoring, that

we must begin by recognizing that it is now quite useless to take apostolic preaching for our model for the simple reason that we do not stand where the Apostles stood, in a world aware of the religious dimension. . . . To-day phrases like "good news of God" are to most people quite meaningless. If the word "god" conveys any meaning at all it is a false one, the sort of thing which Freud would quite rightly dismiss as a "projected father-image" and the Apostles would have thundered against as superstition. Similarly if people to-day do get a "sense of sin" at all it is nothing like the sense of sin among the Jews of the first century A.D.—it is a Freudian guilt-complex, which is a different thing altogether. . . . Belief in these things [the supernatural] should follow, as incidentals almost, from an awareness of a new dimension *in ordinary experience itself*. Separated from that awareness [religious] beliefs like these are only the pathology of the supernatural, which Jesus roundly condemned.

Whether Mr. Wren-Lewis knows it or not, he is only saying what Kierkegaard said years ago: "Preparation for becoming attentive to Christianity does not consist in reading many books but in a deeper immersion in existence." A man becomes aware of his need for God when he is living at a depth where God becomes necessary. Of course a man can live without God if he is content to live on the surface of life. But if he is aware of himself as a human being, if he is essaying the heroic task of being a person in all his relationships, he is brought time and again to the point where he knows his utter insufficiency.

I wish that Dietrich Bonhoeffer had lived long enough to work out the suggestions that he roughed out in his diary and in his letters to a friend, published in 1953 by S.C.M. Press, *Letters and Papers from Prison*:

> To be a Christian does not mean to be religious in a particular way, to cultivate some particular form of asceticism (as a sinner, a penitent or a saint), but to be a man. It is not some religious act which makes a Christian what he is, but participation in the suffering of God in the life of the world. . . . It is only by living completely in this world that one learns to believe. One must abandon every attempt to make something of oneself, whether it be a saint, a converted sinner, a churchman . . . , a righteous man or an unrighteous one, a sick man or a healthy one. This is what I mean by worldliness —taking life in one's stride, with all its duties and problems, its successes and failures, its experiences and helplessness.

The spectacular success of mass evangelism with its thousands of converts coming forward to register a decision is deflecting the Church from its real task. We are willing to pour money, time, and energy into these quick-firing, immediately rewarding campaigns, but not to work patiently together at the slow, difficult job of making ourselves aware. It is not the evangelist we need today so much as the interpreter, the man who will take people where they are and illumine for them the meaning of the ordinary acts of their everyday life, the meaning of their loyalty to family, their sacrifice for their children, their devotion to their jobs, their sense of sportsmanship, and their occasional outbursts of charity.

34

THERE ARE TWO YOUNG PAINTERS IN MY CONGREGATION—NOT Sunday painters exactly, since they are both regular worshipers, but Saturday afternoon painters. One of them is a shipping clerk, the other curiously enough also associated with the sea, a shipwright. In their spare time they produce canvases which are full of energy and fierce color; modern, I suppose people would call them, since they do not pretend to be careful representations of familiar scenes. Last night George, the shipwright, showed me a painting, a study in blues, which while not being a picture of any particular or recognizable ship, conveyed the very essence of shipness. It showed an unfinished hulk, energetically brushed in, with a suggestion of a great whale stranded upon the shore, with all the bones showing. A day or two ago I had admired a picture of Charlie's, again not a recognizable or identifiable woodland scene, but which communicated, to me at least, the sense of struggling life within the woods, the tangled, groping roots, the sense of nature's cathedral, with undertones of the continual battle against evil, the darkness that threatens to extinguish life. I marvel at these two young men and envy their craftsmanship and their vision.

But they will have none of it. Why envy? they cry. You could paint if you only tried. But I protest, and protest not simply on my own behalf but on behalf of their young wives. The lads insist that there is nothing special about what they are doing, and they maintain that their wives, too, should be as creative as they are in the arts. "All you have to do," Charlie kept on saying, "is to put down what you see!" To him it is as simple as that. But as I point out, seeing itself is an art. They assume that we can all see what is there. But most of us are so corrupted, not morally but psychologically, that we do not see what is there. It would take years of unlearning, years of slow, painful practice in using our eyes, to see what is there. Speaking for myself, I tend to see everything at secondhand, through literary spectacles. I do not see the Lake District; I see the Lake District discovered by Wordsworth, Coleridge, and company. I see the snowflake discovered by Francis Thompson:

What heart could have thought you?—
. . . (A filigree petal!)

And I think the same is true in large measure for other people. Men and women were walking about with two perfectly good eyes in their head, but it was Sir Walter Scott who made them aware of the beauty of the Scottish Highlands.

No, my boys, seeing is not as simple a thing as you try to make out. You have the gift of the innocent eye, but I and my like would have to cultivate it.

But I am glad that they go on protesting that people, especially Christian people, should strive to exercise their creative talents. They don't know it, but they are only echoing William Blake, another innocent, who said, "The man who is not an artist is not a Christian." And surely they are right; only they confine creativity to making music, painting pictures, and so forth. For

Blake creativity was a much wider thing than this—he meant the striving to create order out of confusion, to give shape to whatever is shapeless, to put a name to all that is nameless, anonymous, meaningless in our experience, to wrestle with recalcitrant relationships, to turn incidents into events, to bring order, to share the creativity of the God who said over the chaos, Let there be light!

Yes, I am all for encouraging the arts. And perhaps in ages to come the name of Winston Churchill will be known and cherished less for his wartime leadership than for his ability to paint and because he set thousands of humble people following his example. "You saw the studio at Chartwell?" he said when Reginald Pound went to see him. "Did you see *all* the pictures? Each represents happy hours in my life."

For me it is juggling with words that represents creativity. I would like to be a poet, and in my small way I try to be. When I have toiled over sentences and found them forming a picture, when at last they convey exactly what I mean them to do, I get the same satisfaction that Charlie and George get from their painting. The nicest letter I have received lately is a shy tribute to my sermon last Sunday. "What you said last night was more a kind of poem than a sermon. You isolate an aspect of religious revelation or experience and reveal its poetic pattern. . . ." But if that were all, of course, I would be ashamed, not proud. My conscious aim is to reveal through the best words in the best order the beauty and power and illumination of the Word made flesh. There are some people who will never see that beauty or acknowledge that power unless it is revealed, not by a religious salesman, a logical propagandist for the faith, but by a seer and a poet. It was AE, himself a poet, who said, "No church today can convince me that it is inspired unless the words arising from it even in anger break in a storm of beauty on the ear."

35

THE WEAKEST AND MOST PERFUNCTORY ITEM IN A SERVICE OF worship is often the offertory prayer. "Bless these gifts" or "these tokens of our love," or "Prosper the work of the church to which these gifts are devoted," have become clichés which no longer register. Yet with a little imagination this moment in the service is capable of becoming an illuminating and enriching experience. Indeed, an awakening effect can be produced simply by being realistic, that is, instead of talking about "gifts," "offertory," and "tokens," speaking simply and directly about "money." To refer to "this money" is to recall the worshiper to the proper use of all his money. The preacher should unashamedly relate Sunday giving to man's everyday spending and saving and giving. Here are some of the ways in which this may be done:

Lord, as we claim thy blessing upon these gifts, help us so to live and work that all our giving, spending, and saving may meet with thy approval.

Lord of all good life, as we lay this money upon the holy table, deliver us from both the contempt of money and the overvaluing of it.

O God, bless, if thou canst, the ways in which we have earned this money, and accept our thanks for all honorable ways of earning a living; for work that provides us with the wherewithal to share and especially for work that is its own reward.

The dedication of the offering is easily capable of becoming a link with the wider world. Studdert-Kennedy used to insist that we make too little of the offertory and counseled us to plant it firmly within the economic framework of life. "Money is not an evil or sordid thing in itself. There is no greater blessing, nor anything more beautiful than a sound and stable monetary system. The complex network of our modern finance ought to be the healthy nervous system of the body of mankind."

These are some of the ways in which I have tried to bring this home to the man in the pew:

O Lord, behind this offering lies the busy world of our working life—the mill and the factory, the shop and the office. So we ask a blessing upon the commercial and industrial life of our city. Save us from creating a community where wealth accumulates and men decay.

Here, O Lord, we bring together the sacred and the secular, work and worship. As thy Son used bread and wine to show forth thy presence, so help us to use money to create a reconciling and redeeming community.

Sometimes, too, it is a good thing to use the presentation of the offertory to reaffirm our belief in the Church and to link ourselves up with all the varied ministries of Christian men and women—with factory chaplains, army padres, service canteen workers, teachers of divinity, Christian journalists, club leaders, as well as with the more traditional foreign missionary and medical work that goes quietly on day in, day out.

36

PEOPLE WHO REGARD THE NEW TESTAMENT AS A HANDBOOK OF morals must often have a shock when they turn to it seeking guidance for some specific line of conduct which they can follow literally. This came home to me forcibly a few weeks ago when our Parents' Club decided to devote three evenings to the subject of bringing up children in the Christian way. They were full of ideas for the wise and beneficial ordering of family life, drawn from their own experience and from the psychological handbooks they had studied together. But, just to be on the safe side, they asked me to prepare a paper setting forth the New Testament teaching on the subject of family life. Quite obviously they expected me to present them with a large number of texts, setting forth the teaching of Jesus on this important aspect of human life. But in fact, as I explained to them gently, there was no such body of teaching. On the contrary, Jesus of Nazareth did not seem to share our concern for building up family life. He was much more concerned with breaking it down! The texts that immediately spring to mind are sayings concerned with the danger of too much family life, with the disadvantages of family loyalty and solidarity. "He that loveth father or mother more than me . . . If any man come to me, and hate not his father, and mother, and wife, and children . . . Let the dead bury their dead. . . . I am come to set a man at variance against his father, and the daughter against her mother, and the daughter in law against her mother in law."

The fact is that Jesus was facing a very different situation from ours. Family life among the Jews at that time was in no danger of breaking down. It was a close-knit, almost too close-knit, self-contained world. It needed loosening up not building

up. It threatened to become an end in itself, an alternative to that
security and fellowship that can only be found in God. Instead
of being a jumping-off point to the wider world, it had closed in
upon itself. No doubt there are still a few families in the modern
world that are in danger of in-growing, but they are not typical.
Our problem is, not to loosen the family tie that threatens to
strangle rich, full life, but to strengthen it. So if we look to the
New Testament for direct advice on strengthening the family
bond, we are looking in the wrong place.

And this applies to other problems of human behavior also.
Human nature, perhaps, has not changed, but the shape and size
of our problems have changed, and we cannot apply to them the
teaching of Jesus with mechanical rigidity. What we have to do,
rather, is to face our situation with the same thoroughness, the
same concern for the ultimate purpose of God, as that with which
Jesus faced the situation of his day.

37

The Manse, Thursday night

DEAR JACK,

You ask me to tell you frankly whether I think you are a
suitable candidate for the ministry. Maybe I am biased, since I
have known you ever since you were a small boy and I have grown
to love you, delighting in the play of your mind and the deep
seriousness of your spirit. It always surprises me that other people do not find you so attractive as I do. To me it is obvious

that beneath the somewhat aggressive, rather haughty manner you adopt, there is a wealth of quivering sensitivity, a deeply affectionate and humble nature. The trouble, I think, is that those who do not know you well will not stay long enough to find out your real nature. This puts you at a disadvantage, which you must learn to recognize and to remedy. You must be humble enough to realize that people cannot wait for your best qualities to unfold in the warmth of their approbation. Perhaps, I suggest this tentatively, your unwillingness to make an immediate good impression is a form of pride. Like some women who hate to think that they are loved simply for the accident of their good looks, you scorn to be approved and esteemed simply for your surface qualities. Like treasure hid in a field, you think the good stuff within you is worth the labor of digging out!

When you told me last night that you were thinking of offering your services to the Church, I was pleased—and uneasy. I wonder why. I have been wondering all day. You have many of the gifts that make for a successful ministry; you have a fine presence, a good voice, a subtle mind, and a strength of purpose that has proved itself in the job you now hold. But the unworthy suspicion sometimes crosses my mind that you are seeking an outlet for self-expression, and you think you will find it in a pulpit. Do not misunderstand me, lad; of course a man will hardly make a success of the ministry unless he has a desire to create, a real urge to "rivet and publish himself of his own personality," as Walt Whitman puts it. I am not afraid of that. Without it, and without a delight in putting his ideas into words and of sharing his insights, discoveries, and experiences, a man who is to occupy a pulpit week by week, who is called upon to make and preach a hundred sermons a year, will find the ministry a dragging burden. I have heard you preach three times. Like a great many other young speakers, you are at present intent on shocking people, being provocative and "daring." That's natural in a young fellow of your age; you feel you have something new to say and that the old fogies in the church need stabbing into new life. They have been fed on commonplaces and platitudes long enough. What am I afraid of then? That you will go on avoiding commonplaces and platitudes, not because they are false but because they are old, that you will succumb to the temptation to be original about everything, even at the cost of ignoring the obvious truth and to the point of slightly distorting every subject you touch for the sake of dramatic effectiveness. I would like to feel that you are humble enough to be the servant of great ideas rather than the exploiter and manipulator of outrageous opinions. At present you give me the impression of being more concerned to tell what you think of Jesus Christ than of what Jesus Christ thinks of you. But I am quite sure that this is a phase that will pass. Like Canon Raven the years will bring you to the point where you will pity the man "who does not find God more interesting than his own soul." Believe me, your stock of original ideas and your peculiar slant of vision will soon exhaust itself, and the day will come when the chief interest and the absorbing passion of your life will be to discover, to expose yourself to, to interpret, the insights and ideas of Christ, and to report what he has done, and can do, for your soul.

At the moment, like many a young would-be preacher, you tend to see yourself as a "prophet." The Church is there to be preached at, to be reformed and exhorted, to be the background against which you perform your lonely office. If you ever do enter the ministry, you will soon find that such a conception does not wear well. You will find that your best work is done as a minister within the Church, with the Church, and for the Church. You will find that the deepest joy comes from sharing life with others, from encouraging others to discharge their ministry. Pray that God will give you a pastoral heart, for without this the ministry will become a frustrating experience. People who begin by being prima donnas of the pulpit mostly end by becoming scolds, haranguing and nagging their congregations.

You asked me to be frank. I hope I have not hurt you by my plain speaking. You know me well enough to realize that I consider the ministry to be the finest job in the world. I do not envy any man, but I think I have learned something from my own mistakes, and in writing this letter to you I am really writing to the ghost of my own youth. Nothing would give me greater pride than to officiate one day at your ordination service, but I want to be there with you as a servant of Jesus Christ, as an "ambassador in bonds," working and serving within the limits of truth and fellowship.

Believe me to be,

Your minister and friend,
PETER PARSON

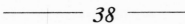

38

THE MAIN ITEM ON THE AGENDA OF THE LOCAL YOUTH COM-
mittee today was "The Problem of Un-clubbable Youth." I had to look twice before I got it into focus. Un-clubbable youth! There is, it seems, something sinister about a boy who likes his

own company. Henceforth the nongregarious and the shy must add to their disability a feeling of guilt.

The members of the committee were mostly parsons, club leaders, scoutmasters, and settlement heads, and, to do them justice, they were thinking of that hard core of adolescent boys and girls who hang about street corners or drift aimlessly around in gangs. There are people who prefer to mill around under their own steam, or to gather in dubious "caffs," to being catered for in bright and well-organized clubs. But as the debate proceeded, I began to wonder whether I had any right to be on the committee, since I could not suppress a feeling of sympathy with people of any age who refuse to be organized. Street corner gangs sometimes get into trouble: to the cold eye of the onlooker they seem undisciplined and rowdy; they shout and sing and jostle one another into the gutter; they use pretty strong language occasionally. But after nearly twenty years in downtown areas I happen to know that many of them are harmless enough; their conversation leaves much to be desired in depth and finesse, but in their own rough and ready way they discuss pretty nearly everything under the sun, the street corner and the snack bar being their university common room.

I was surprised that nobody thought of asking why these youngsters prefer the shelter of a drafty doorway or the fug of a "caff" to the facilities so freely offered by clubs and settlements. Perhaps if they were articulate, they would answer in the words of John Ruskin writing to his friend Charles Eliot Norton: "You want to do me good like all my other friends . . . but good in your way and not in mine." It is hardly likely that they will have heard of Hobab, the brother-in-law of Moses, who, when approached with the words "Come thou with us, and we will do thee good," angrily shrugged off his do-good relative (scenting patronage no doubt). Moses, however, won him over when he complimented him on his skill and his knowledge of the lay of the land, saying, "Be to us instead of eyes"; we need the something you alone can give us in our journey to the Promised Land. The spirit of Hobab, nevertheless, persists.

What really got my goat, however, was the easy assumption made by one speaker after another that *all* young people who failed to link up with an organization were either antisocial or maladjusted. Are there not thousands of bright and purposeful adolescents who actually prefer to be alone? who want to work things out in their own way? Things have come to a pretty pass when such people have to apologize for their existence. It is often from such people, lonely, moody, brooding, introspective, that society recruits its poets and creative scientists. And is there no danger in being too well integrated with the herd? I fancy that the best thing that could happen to some adjusted people would be to be thrown into confusion, to be forced into some sort of secret interior dialogue.

And I wonder how much genius and really creative thinking runs out into the sand because by and large most people are never alone. I was still in my early teens when one day on a wild, deserted stretch of the Gower Coast I met a famous preacher, a man renowned for his spacious oratory and penetrating speech in the pulpits of the principality. Even as a boy I realized that there was probably some connection between his amazing power to hold the crowds and his withdrawal from them; that it was on these long, withdrawn, lonely walks on the seashore that he tapped the deep wells of thought. If a man is to earn the title of thinker, he must be much alone. But the trend today, even in the ministry, is all the other way; the call is for good mixers, men of bright and ready address. Walt Whitman used to test the strength and soundness of the lines of *Leaves of Grass* by flinging them up into the air and shouting them against the roar of the waves on Long Island. As Nietzsche said, no idea can be true unless it is thought in the open air, and he might have added, unless it comes from the unhurried, secret life of a man who is much alone.

39

WE IMAGINE THAT WE DIFFER FROM PEOPLE ON MATTERS OF principle when, in fact, we have only failed to get their wave length. Perhaps what makes us ill at ease with old Jones is not that he is a bigoted old fool, but that his mind works at a different speed from ours. We fail to allow for a difference in life tempo. The psychologists have warned us that what disrupts a personal relationship may be some hidden factor, a deeply buried incompatibility, or underground desires and aims that are banished from sight. But while the psychologists have been busy dredging these bits of wreckage from the great depths, they have, so it seems to me, been neglecting matters lying just immediately below the surface. One of these matters, I am increasingly persuaded, is the rate at which different people live, think, come to decisions. It may be this, and not rational disagreement, that creates difficulties. We all know theoretically that some people mature later than others, though we seldom make use of this theoretical knowledge in our dealings with them. In the same way, though we may realize intellectually that Jones's mind creaks to

95

its conclusions with the ponderous speed of a steam roller and that Brown's mind is all quicksilver and lightning, in our practical dealings with both we may quite ignore this factor of personal speed. Incidentally, there might even be national and racial factors involved here. Mary Colum fancied that in France time went further and that the days were three times as long as in America. "There seemed to be endless time on our hands, time for work, time for idleness, time for recreation."

If I am right, I hope I shall begin to achieve a new understanding with certain people with whom my previous contacts have been sterile and frustrating. Was it, I begin to wonder, my fault that I found old Jones such a bigot? Perhaps I should have given him more time to articulate and express himself. My impatience may have caused him to stiffen; by forcing the pace of his thought perhaps I caused him to become more obstinate and dogmatic than he really is. Here is something I must watch.

Perhaps this question of individual speed should receive more attention from evangelists than it has done hitherto. By pressing for a spot decision are we not ignoring the personal tempo of a particular life? Some people need space and time in which to grow. It may even be that a period in the wilderness of doubt is an absolute necessity if they are to mature in accordance with their own life rate. As I look back on my own ministry, I see that it is the people who came to maturity slowly who are lasting best. Desmond MacCarthy once wrote in reviewing Aldous Huxley's *Grey Eminence,* "I am always suspicious of writers who, having found Truth, attempt to convert others before they have tried hard for years to live by that Truth themselves." Last week, visiting the scene of one of my former pastorates, I met several young men with whom I thought I had absolutely failed; after nine years' solid work with them in church and Bible Class and Youth Club, they appeared to have drifted away. But I discovered, lunching in Long Acre with one, a young sporting journalist, that he was even now in process of seeking confirmation at the hands of the bishop of Southwark after an arid period of negation through which he had never quite let go of what he was pleased to call my teaching and influence. Laus Deo! And that same evening I called on a rising young electronics engineer, whose army service and long years of arduous study had uprooted him from the church of his boyhood, who is quietly and firmly rooted in the Christian faith, matured slowly and almost in an underground fashion, but deep, and I am firmly persuaded, lasting. Neither of these two lads, and I could cite others, could, or should, have been hurried. I came away from both remembering the words of Isaiah, "He that believeth shall not make haste."

40

THERE IS SUCH A THING AS PREACHING OVER PEOPLE'S HEADS. (Personally I don't think we do enough of it. I like Willard Sperry's reminiscence of the old preacher under whom he served in a mill-city parish. The old man was accustomed to preach once a year on the discoveries in astronomy made during the previous twelve months. Sperry protested, "Here in this city where everybody is busy making and selling cotton cloth, of what use is your annual sermon on the stars?" He smiled and said, "No use at all, dear boy, but it greatly enlarges my idea of God.")

But preaching over people's heads is one thing; preaching beyond their problems is another. Much of the preaching I have heard lately grossly overestimates the capacity of the ordinary man for sinning. It treats him as if he were a great sinner, whereas most of us are, to use the language of the *Prayer Book,* "miserable sinners," miserable not least in the triviality of the temptations that assail us and the sins we commit. The man in the pulpit addresses us as if we were passionate, dark souls, like Augustine of Hippo, whereas, strictly speaking, the tides of passion run very thin in us. Tonight the last hymn in the service contained this couplet:

> Such dire offences to forgive,
> Such guilty, daring souls to spare—

and I felt, as I sang it, that I was wearing an overcoat several sizes too large for me. Guilty I may be, but hardly daring; hardly the deliberate willful rebel that the hymn envisaged.

When William Temple was a student at Oxford, he attended an evangelistic meeting at which the visiting American preacher pressed upon the congregation the forgiveness of God, quoting the text, "Though your sins be as scarlet, they shall be as white as snow." Temple said, "He was not talking to my condition at all. My sins are not scarlet; they are gray—all gray." I think most of us could echo Temple's melancholy confession; the sins from which we suffer are not big, dramatic acts of self-affirmation, but drab, tired sins, sins of inertia, laziness, timidity, sins that arise from our refusal to be creative, to be richly and fully human.

When one faces a normal congregation, there may indeed be "guilty, daring souls" to rebuke and restrain, but mostly one senses the presence of people who need encouragement, encouragement to be bolder, more confident, more daring, to make more of themselves than they have yet attempted. It is not "sins" that they are suffering from, but such maladies of the soul as boredom. Yet in a whole lifetime of listening to preachers I have never heard a sermon on boredom, not one! But how right Kierkegaard is when he says, "Boredom is the root of all evil," boredom which he defines as the "despairing refusal to be oneself."

41

THE AMERICANS HAVE AN EXPRESSIVE SLANG TERM—"SACRED cow"—to denote a subject which it is considered bad form or even blasphemy to criticize. I sometimes think that one of the sacred cows of ecclesiastical life is the Sunday school. People are quite willing to criticize this or that detail, to admit that some Sunday schools are badly organized, but how few church folk are willing to entertain, even for purposes of discussion, the suggestion that the Sunday school itself is a mistake. Hoskins tried to introduce this topic at our last fraternal, but there were no takers. It is taken for granted that it belongs to the structure of church life, that church life could not get along without it despite the fact that the institution is less than two hundred years old and that the education of boys and girls in the faith proceeded fairly satisfactorily in the absence of formal religious instruction.

As I pointed out to Hoskins, the Sunday school is, like so many other modern innovations and "improvements," such as community centers, youth clubs, and the like, an evidence of the breakdown of healthy family life. Given the present attenuated state of the average "Christian" home, the Sunday school may be an absolute necessity, but we should never forget that it is a very second best. Religious instruction should be carried on in the bosom of the family by the natural teachers of young people, namely, their parents.

I think that most parents, if they took up the position they have abdicated, would have enough sense to realize something that the Sunday schools, working in isolation from the normal life of the child, do not realize. I mean that the New Testament is far beyond the mental and spiritual grasp of the child. We would never dream of teaching small children Aristotle's *Ethics* or leading them through a course in Plato's *Republic,* yet we take it for granted that tiny tots in the Sunday school may be introduced to the sayings and deeds of the profoundest religious and ethical teacher who ever lived, and that they have the capacity to grasp the meaning of his extraordinary life.

If I had my way, children up to the age of ten certainly, and perhaps beyond that, would be brought up on the Old Testament exclusively. I would not allow them to touch, much less discuss, the New until they were in their teens. The Old Testament stories belong to the childhood of the nation, and they belong to the childhood of the individual. A little boy struggling to assert himself is only hampered in his proper psychological development by being introduced to the mature ethics of Jesus, an ethics which demands an experience of life and a sensitiveness which it would be wrong to expect from a child passing through the "gang" stage. The insights of Jesus are for grown men and women, and we succeed only in making hypocrites out of children when we expect them to approve of and applaud and practice the way of nonresistance, creative forgiveness, and redeeming love. I cannot help feeling that the time to meet the Sermon on the Mount and to experience its full impact is in the middle twenties, and that it is a positive handicap to have known, and falsely imagined that one understood, the words from one's early childhood.

Many recent converts to the Christian faith have experienced it in greater depth than people brought up within the fold precisely because, it seems to me, they had nothing to unlearn, no deadly familiarity with the figure and words of Jesus to overcome. "I grew up in complete isolation from the Christian faith, as a member of a family which had entirely abandoned both the practice and profession of religion," writes J. V. Langmead Casserley, who is nowadays proving so attractive and persuasive an apologist for religion. "No church, no Sunday school, no prayers at my mother's knee, just the pleasant existence of a spoiled child in moderately prosperous circumstances, growing up in a spiritual vacuum, as jealously guarded against the love of God as against the sins of men." Rom Landau has given the same kind of testimony. And it makes one wonder whether the boasted advantages of a Christian upbringing are not greatly overrated.

Goethe in *Wilhelm Meister's Travels* outlines his ideal system of religious education. First children should be introduced to religion through song and story and through acquaintance with pictures, particularly of the exploits and achievements of the Israelites.

Their Sacred Books stand so happily combined together, that even out of the most diverse elements, the feeling of a whole still rises before us. They are complete enough to satisfy; fragmentary enough to excite; barbarous enough to rouse; tender enough to appease; and for how many other contradictory merits might not these Books, might not this one Book, be praised!

The New Testament is reserved in Goethe's scheme for those who grow up with some thoughtfulness of temper. Each pupil is given enough that he may know where more is to be had, should such a want spring up within him. The sufferings of Christ are not paraded, but held in reserve.

We draw a veil over those sufferings precisely because we reverence them so highly. We hold it a damnable audacity to bring forth that torturing Cross, and the Holy One who suffers upon it, or to expose them to the light of the sun, which hid its face when a reckless world forced such a sight on it; to make these mysterious secrets, in which the divine depth of Sorrow lies hid, and play with them, fondle them, trick them out, and rest not till the most reverent of all solemnities appears vulgar and paltry.

42

WHAT PART DOES TEMPERAMENT PLAY IN SHAPING A MAN'S theology? Yesterday I chanced to meet three people whose particular brand of theology fitted their temperament like a glove. Horace Steel, for example, is a rigid dogmatist who sees the Christian life as a series of clear-cut positions, a total and uncompromising surrender of himself to Christ the Redeemer. But then he is by nature a dark soul, a seething caldron of a man, who has all his work cut out to keep his gusty, passionate, emotional nature from running away with him. Christianity for him is subjection—passionate and utter obedience—with no room for if's and but's. He is impatient with tentative people, with people who want to think it out. He thinks they are stalling, and so they would be if they had his temperament. But a man like David Church is a much more easygoing person. By nature he is sweetly reasonable, appreciative of the good things of life and able to handle them with grace and enjoyment. For him "creation" and "incarnation" are more meaningful words than "original sin" and "redemption." In becoming a Christian he did not repudiate his past experience; he learned to interpret it and to deepen it. Far from sharing Horace Steel's suspicion of tentativeness and search, he suspects all that is final, dogmatic, and closed. He has not "found Christ," he explains, but is continually "finding" him and refinding him in all the groping, seeking, impromptu, and improvising living of each day. My Irish friend Robert Buckmaster, on the other hand, being temperamentally aggressive, delighting in a scrap, never happier than when he is on a crusade, is a Christian warrior for whom religion is a battle with the forces of evil. My own temperament leads me to be conciliatory, to look always for the mediating way. I tend to regard the most important word in the Christian vocabulary as the word "reconciliation" and to base my theology upon the fact of Christ "reconciling the world unto himself." But obviously that is as one-sided a theology as the other three; we are all distorted and incomplete theologians. This would not matter perhaps if we could agree to differ, but we all want to claim finality and completeness for our partial insights.

And what a variety of temperaments the parson faces as he stands up in the pulpit to preach! The easygoing and the strenuous, the tidy-minded and the people who delight in chiaroscuro, the traditionalist and the innovator, the matter-of-fact and the fanciful, the legalists and the sentimentalists, the stolid and the mercurial—each taking from his message what he wants to hear and interpreting what he hears in accordance with his own needs. It's a wonder that anything ever gets across! And yet this is the miracle of preaching: that sometimes this mixed assortment of types is wonderfully welded into a unity, becomes, as it were, one listening ear.

--------- *43* ---------

THE EASIEST WAY TO PRICK A PARSON'S CONSCIENCE IS TO TALK to him about private prayer. I have never met a minister who feels satisfied that he is giving enough time or thought to his own practice of prayer. So when Dr. Henderson addressed the fraternal this afternoon on "The Minister's Devotional Life," we were all prepared to feel guilty. In the rush of sermon preparation, visiting, administration, and committee work it is perilously easy to confine one's praying to the pulpit or to make do with the sketchiest daily meditation.

The doctor gave us a choice essay on the masters of the spiritual life, paying particular attention to St. Theresa's *The Interior Castle* and *The Way of Perfection,* and *The Dark Night of the Soul* by St. John of the Cross. But such is the perversity of my nature, the more he talked about the methods of the saints, the more rebellious I became. As he analyzed the phases of the mystic way, purgation, illumination, union; as he dealt earnestly and wistfully with "spiritual dryness" and the "temptations of the spiritual life," I was moved to inward protest, and when the time came for discussion, I had to give vent to my feelings.

"It is true enough," I said, "that the Roman Catholics possess great riches of experience and wisdom for the cultivation of the spiritual life. Compared with them we Protestants are slovenly and amateurish. But if we are to improve our devotional practice, ought we not to do it within a Protestant framework instead of trying to improvise within a Roman Catholic framework? There is a Protestant attitude to life—to the life of the spirit and to the life of the world around us, but you are urging us to express that attitude within a structure that is foreign to us. The Roman Catholic prays within a hierarchical structure, wherein a sharp distinction is made between laity and priesthood; where within the priesthood itself a distinction is made between the 'religious,' dedicated to prayer and contemplation, and the 'secular,' charged with the cure of souls in a parish. For us these distinctions do not exist; we must do our praying within the framework of the 'priesthood of all believers.' We ministers have to realize our fellowship with God, not in the cloister, but as we undertake 101 jobs of parish life; not in silence and withdrawal, but in full identity and community with our fellow church members. In the Roman Catholic manuals a great place is given to the practice of self-examination and ruthless self-scrutiny; we come to the process of self-discovery, not by solitary introspection, but through our encounter in full richness with our fellow Christians. We learn to know ourselves as we are tested in fellowship; our spiritual weak places are revealed as we strive to meet the needs of men and to become their friends and helpers. And as for discipline we do not require to invent methods of discipline; life itself provides all the disciplines that are necessary. Any minister who is dealing faithfully with his people finds that the calls upon his sympathy, his honesty, his patience and self-effacement, call for a discipline more arduous than the hair shirt and physical flagellation."

After I had rambled on like this for some time, I was set upon by some of the younger men, but received unexpected support from the oldest member of the fraternal, a retired missionary of eighty-four, a man of humble and saintly spirit whom we all imagined had a richly fed devotional life. "I am interested in what you say, Peter," he said. "All my life I have felt worried about my poor attempts to regulate and improve my prayer life. I have felt guilty about my distaste for the monastic literature recommended to me. I also believe that we ought to create the devotional structures in which the Protestant attitude may express itself and realize itself. But how do we do that? Is there any literature on the subject?"

The only book I know that tries to wrestle with the shaping of a really Protestant prayer practice is a little volume of Malcolm Spencer's, *Vitality,* published by S.C.M. Press way back in 1931 and afterward reissued in paper covers, though it never attained a great sale, I think. I have bought and given away a dozen copies of this little book, but only to people whose minds are flexible, who are not afraid of an unfamiliar phrase. People who look for rules and regulations and stereotyped ritual would hardly find it to their taste. It takes seriously the belief to which we all pay lip service, that God is the living God, active in the whole range of life, that he may be apprehended by the senses, the imagination, the mind, and the spirit. Prayer is not a preparation for living; it is the appreciation of the divine life wherever it is manifested. We do not discover God in prayer and thereafter take him with us into our daily work, our leisure and companionships. It is in daily work, in the creative use of leisure, in the fullest exercise of friendship, that he reveals himself and that he gives himself to us. We pray most really when we live most deeply. Of course there will be special periods of withdrawal and set times for conscious recollection, but these are but the beginnings of prayer, not its end. As Malcolm Spencer puts it:

To begin with the daily regimen: we should not let ourselves loose on the world until we are thoroughly awake to the romantic possibilities of the day before us, tingling with the anticipation of the manifold opportunities of a living world: alive to the appeal of natural beauty, and to the fact of our bodies as instruments for its appreciation; alive to the beauty of human artifice, human intercourse, human arts and crafts and institutions; alive to the interests of work, the opportunities of personal service, the fascination of social progress; alive to the growth of Christ's kingdom in personal and public life and to the ever closer fellowship of Christian with Christian in consecrated purpose and self-denying effort.

Just as for the Protestant faith is not belief in static propositions or the mental assent to information about God, but a dynamic, daily renewed practice of fellowship with God, so prayer is less the performance of certain rites than an uplifting of the whole personality to God. It is response in conscious, deliberate, and deeply appreciative action to whatever meets us in the day's work, whatever challenges us by its stubbornness or difficulty, to whatever seeks to enlist us for joy, beauty, and truth, whatever makes claims upon us in the interest of friendship and love.

44

"GIVE ME YOUR HONEST OPINION OF THIS MODERN POETRY."
George Harrison was poking around my bookshelves today. Out
of the corner of my eye I had been watching him dip into several
of the slim volumes of Eliot, Auden, Spender, Day Lewis, and
Edwin Muir that make a gay break in the solid wall of standard
poets, Oxford anthologies, and presentation-bound Miltons,
Wordsworths, and Shelleys. "Surely there is nothing here that you
can quote from the pulpit?" he queried. "In my young days
preachers drew freely on the works of Tennyson and Browning.
The more daring of them preached sermons on Francis Thompson's *Hound of Heaven* and quoted extensively from his other
works. I remember the publication of John Masefield's *The Everlasting Mercy*—that was a sheer gift to the preacher; that was
the last modern poetry that a preacher could use. But this modern
stuff is unquotable; it doesn't sing; it doesn't lend itself to decla-
mation; it isn't even intelligible. I doubt if you could find four
lines in your favorite, Auden, to drive home a point or round off
a peroration."

He is right of course—on his own premises. Apart from some
isolated lines in *The Rock,* which Eliot wrote for the church, some
few things in *The Four Quartets,* two or three extracts from
Auden's *The Age of Anxiety* or *New Year Letter,* a phrase or
two from Edwin Muir's "Soliloquy," I do not recall using anything directly in the pulpit.

But the modern preacher has a greater ally in the modern poet
than the Victorian preacher had in the Victorian poet. The Vic-
torians and the Georgians may have been better singers, but they
were lyricizing the obvious. For the most part they were saying in

verse what everybody knew and what everybody agreed with, and they were writing for the same public as the preacher himself. But today the situation is otherwise. The modern poet is addressing a different public; he is speaking to people not within sound of the preacher's voice. If, therefore, he has any religious insights, any religious "message," to communicate, he is a fellow worker of the preacher's, laboring in a different vineyard. Many of our contemporaries who would not be seen dead in church are listening, and listening hard, to whatever it is that Eliot and Auden have to say. It is part of Eliot's declared purpose through such plays as *The Cocktail Party, The Family Reunion,* and *The Confidential Clerk* to get the ear of the unchurched, to proclaim the Christian message in contemporary terms.

Even where the poet is not a committed Christian, but like Muir a deeply religious man, or like Spender a humanist, the preacher will do well to listen to him, because he is enlarging the self-consciousness of modern man. He is making us aware of the depersonalization and dehumanization wrought in us by the mass culture and the trash culture of our time. Writing of the American poet Conrad Aiken, Henry A. Murray says:

The writer is the super-sensitive, the super-perceptive and the super-expressive one, the first to feel the strain, the wrong, the lie, the nastiness and the dearth, the first to weep, to warn, to rebuke, to rebel, or to egress, and, also, the first to perceive the new promise, the hope, the sharable vision, incarnate in a single act or word, or in a life. What a profound poet feels and perceives to-day, Everyman will feel and perceive to-morrow or several generations hence.

The moderns may not provide us with tags or with quotations, but where they are deeply sensitive and deeply wounded by the modern spirit, they can sharpen our understanding and make us aware of what our coarser spirits, our custom-lidded eyes, have been unable to perceive. That has always been the function of the poet—to make us aware, to make us see more, to understand and to enjoy more. Our major poets are men with the courage to immerse themselves in all the doubt and uncertainty and chaos of the modern world. They do not merely analyze it in the objective, superior manner of some pulpiteers; they experience it. They enter the Waste Land and emerge, thin, wan, hollow-eyed, to report on what we have only sensed from afar off. They have pushed doubt and negation to their extreme limit.

Can anyone read the modern poets I have mentioned without being probed, without being forced to ask ultimate questions? Though we never quote a line from them, they help us to understand the dilemmas of modern life and the plight of modern man; they enable us to direct the answers of Christianity to the right questions. They will not give us pulpit platitudes in rhyming form, but they will give us a public to whom the answers provided by our gospel will be relevant; they prepare the ground into which the good seed can fall.

It is a thousand pities that the churchgoing public shies away from the modern poets, that they prefer the easy rhymes of Ella Wheeler Wilcox or Edgar Guest to the hard but rewarding business of grappling with the moderns. Amos Wilder has well said:

If the reader has not evaded the modern spiritual situation, or lived on its margin, if he has been responsibly concerned with the deeper dilemmas and anguish, public and intimate, of our century, and has had some interest in and understanding of the nature of art, he will find that the modern poet or artist speaks to him.

Maybe the trouble is, as Wilder suggests, that we are not willing to live through the costs that illuminate our lives. The artist and the poet have paid the price, they have exposed mind and heart and nerves to the full fury of our stormy decades, but they will be meaningful only to those who approach them in the same spirit.

45

RECENTLY I HAVE FOUND MYSELF GIVING MORE SPACE IN THE Sunday services to readings from the historical narrative of the Old Testament. At one time I confined my Old Testament readings to the devotional and inspirational parts of the book, to the Psalms and the Prophets, under the impression that these were edifying and spoke to the timeless needs of the congregation. But lately I have been making much more use of the purely factual and historical parts, to the wanderings and doings of the Children of Israel.

This is due partly to a deeper understanding of the Bible, thanks to recent Old Testament scholarship; and partly to the fact that I have been looking back over my own youth and realizing how much poorer it would have been without the framework which the history of the Chosen Race provided for the interpretation of my own experience. Bondage in Egypt, the Deliverance, the Exodus, and the years in the wilderness, during which the rabble of Jewish tribes were forged into a people. These were not simply events in the history of a people called the Jews; they provided a structure into which I was able to fit my own growing life and to find illumination upon my personal history. I am interested to

111

see that Bernard Eugene Meland, the American theologian, testifies
to the same thing:

Faith preceded and underlies the structure of philosophy, in the
individual as in the culture. This is certainly true in my case. The
Biblical drama of redemption, from the Exodus to the Cross and Res-
surrection of Jesus Christ, forms the earliest chain of childhood
images of which I have any conscious recollection. I do not know
a time in my personal history when this imagery did not shape what
thoughts I had concerning the beginnings of my life and my own
destiny. These tales held a charm for me in my childhood, as they
undoubtedly have done for many children through the long years of
the race. In this respect I was literally a child of the Christian community, whose mind and spirit was cradled and nurtured by its formative
myth.

Pierre Emmanuel, the French Catholic poet, sees this emphasis
on the biblical story as the chief glory of Protestantism. In his
entrancing autobiography, *The Universal Singular,* he says:

The Bible, as the Protestants read it, makes them contemporary
with a history that Catholics have made the mistake of embalming.
. . . The minister opened the Bible—of which we Catholics knew
nothing—and the strong voice was raised with the authority of the
ages. I knew only the Sunday Gospel, which had become a sort of
popular broadsheet for our religion, and had been disfigured, besides, by innumerable commentaries. . . . But I knew nothing of the
Old Testament, of the Epistles, nor of the Apocalypse. Now, however, I saw that these texts made up the single indivisible fabric of
the very words of Christ. . . . It was through the Bible that I understood the synoptic character of history. It may be read both as a
series of events and as a simultaneous drama. The Protestants, in
their sermons and prayers, take it all in at one glance and centre it

upon Christ . . . the individual drama is united with the drama of the species. The whole struggle between eternity and time takes place in the whole race and in the deep ego.

And so I see now that in concentrating upon those parts of the Old Testament that are immediately "uplifting" and that can provide, as it were, a generalized atmosphere of devotion and inspiration, I have been depriving my people of the strong and abiding framework in which their inner life might be nourished. The inner life of man is nourished not on information, but upon symbolism, myths and legends, dramas and poems, and it is by no accident that the poets of today are turning back to the old Greek and Indian myths or inventing myths with the aid of psychology, so as to feed the wasted spirit of man. But here in the Bible story is the greatest "myth" of all time, no mere poetic metaphor or invention, but a matter of hard historical fact.

46

SEX BECOMES A PROBLEM WHEN IT IS WRENCHED OUT OF ITS context. And its true context is not duty, or the rearing of children, or family life, important as these are; the true context of sex is joy.

The Creator has shared with his children the gift of creation; man seeks to exercise that gift out of frustration, or to compensate for a feeling of inferiority, or as a means to some end, whereas of

the Creator it was said that he saw everything that he had made
and pronounced it good, and that at creation "the morning stars
sang together, and all the sons of God shouted for joy."

What do we find at the basis of unhappy or strained sexual
relationships? That one or other of the partners is having recourse
to physical intimacy out of a feeling of frustration, or in order to
forget, or to flee from a feeling of inadequacy or disappointment.
Instead of being a celebration, the act becomes a means of escape
or of forgetfulness; it proceeds not from health but from disease,
not out of strength but out of weakness, not from joy and health
but from exasperation or self-pity. And the result is that one of the
partners feels that he or she is being used as a thing, a drug, a
medicine, or as a hot-water bottle, is being prostituted as a person.

As a young and happily married man said to me last night, "I
love my wife, and at moments when we have achieved real fellowship in mind and spirit, when we have had a good day together,
I turn to her in complete happiness to fulfill and consummate that
deep, rich joy we have had in each other. But I am unhappy and
somewhat repelled when Elizabeth, having had a frustrated day,
feeling disappointed with herself or being self-distrustful about
her career, turns to the physical act in order to forget it all, in
order to compensate for the happiness she feels she has missed on
another level."

This is not an isolated case. And what is really happening is
that people are using the flesh in order to solve the problems of
the spirit. They obtain a momentary relief from the tension of
self. But the relief is only a semblance of the true atonement. What
is experienced is not spiritual identity with the loved one, but a
momentary escape from separateness in the darkness of the unconscious. And so, far from being permanently enriched and

cleansed by this experience, the self returns to the daylight world fundamentally unchanged, if not indeed corrupted.

Somebody once said that two people have no chance of being successfully married to each other if they are not already married to themselves. Of course we are incomplete as we are, and marriage wonderfully fulfills and integrates our lives. But it is the total experience of being married that does this, not one isolated act. People expect from physical union what can come only from growth and discipline at other levels. And so sex becomes an attempt to redeem the self instead of a sharing of the redeemed self.

47

I AM PLANNING A SERIES OF SERMONS ON "EDUCATING THE Emotions." Why not? We teach people how to think, but not how to feel. We take it for granted that the mental life of man needs to be trained, but we assume that his feelings can look after themselves. As a result one is constantly meeting people who are sensitive to ideas and quick to detect a false syllogism, but whose emotional life is crude and chaotic. Many a man would wince at a weak argument who would accept an unreal feeling without protest. Our response to beauty, our use of the senses, our life in the imagination, are poor and unregulated compared with our intellectual grasp of things. Twenty-five years ago I heard John Macmurray say in his broadcast talks, afterward published as

Freedom in the Modern World: "If our thought is orderly and sane in comparison with our feelings, that is only because we have cultivated and trained our minds and neglected the training of our emotional life." That sentence has never ceased to trouble my mind.

Since those words were spoken, things have gone from bad to worse. Our educational practice as apart from our theory grows more and more rational and mechanical, designed to produce that never-ending stream of technicians and machine minders which our society demands if it is to keep up its standard of living. The emphasis is almost all on "useful knowledge," on sharpening the speculative and critical intellect. Consequently we are turning out people who are quick-witted and slow of heart, mentally full and emotionally empty, their heads stuffed with information and their hearts starved. It is this that partly accounts for the upsurge of violence among the working-class boys of our sprawling cities and the middle-class appetite for violence at secondhand through films and fiction.

By "educating the emotions," I do not mean educating them out of existence. What is wanted is, not a technique for repressing, taming, and throttling the rich instinctive life within, but teaching concerning its use and enjoyment. We have heard too much talk about controlling the feelings and not enough about deepening and purifying them, so that they might suffuse and energize our thinking and raise it to a loftier power. We need, in Lawrence Hyde's words, "to think organically, doing justice, not only to our logical findings, but also to our intuitions and our emotional responses."

I used to think that this problem was peculiar to the West, aggravated by our teeming, impersonal city life and the necessity of conforming to the machine. But the cry for emotional nurture and training comes from the very heart of Africa! John Taylor, who has spent many years as a teacher in Uganda, reporting on his experiences there, says:

It is a sad and shameful thing, that with so much of the education of African children in the hands of the Church, we have done so little to train the emotional side of their life. We have given them a largely cerebral Christianity. The majority of the younger generation of African Christians do their thinking in the class-room, but they do their feeling in the village.

Perhaps we are in a better position, a more humble frame of mind, to listen to that wild man D. H. Lawrence than we were a quarter of a century ago. He said then in his essay on John Galsworthy: "A man who is *emotionally* educated is as rare as a phoenix. The more scholastically educated a man is generally, the more he is an emotional boor." But naturally we reject his prescription, which is to plunge into the dark, rich instinctive life of the body, to seek forgetfulness from our accursed self-consciousness and ubiquitous rationality in the flesh.

But one looks in vain for any guidance, or indeed for any real awareness of the problem, from the literature that pours in a never-ending stream from the presses of our denominational headquarters. The education directors of the Protestant denominations seem to envisage the kingdom of heaven as one vast study group. They send out innumerable pamphlets on the Christian attitude to Communism but none on the Christian use of the imagination, helps to the study of the Bible but none on the care and cultivation of the senses. The whole approach is argumentative, rational, and logical.

It is perhaps time that we Protestants preached fewer sermons on "The truth shall make you free" and more on "Out of the depths have I cried unto thee, O Lord." Indeed, does not our whole attitude to preaching need to be re-examined? The sermon in a typical Protestant church is an argument to be followed, whereas it ought to be an event to be experienced. And more time and thought need to be given to a recovery of the lost art of contemplation and meditation.

The easy way, of course, would be to adopt the Roman Catholic modes of worship, to introduce more color and pageantry, more "dim religious light," to work directly upon the emotions of awe and wonder through the use of pictures, incense, and movement. But there is a difference between inducing feelings of reverence and awe and mystery, and centering the emotions upon God. We must be true to our Protestant insight that the deepest and richest emotions are stirred by direct confrontation with a Person, and we must seek means for allowing that confrontation to take place. If the Roman Catholic temptation is to enjoy one's feelings about religion, the Protestant temptation is to substitute ideas about God for fellowship with him. Here, I feel, we could draw much more than we have done on the help already given to us by Martin Buber in his truly seminal book *I and Thou*.

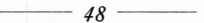

48

IT IS MORE IMPORTANT TO LISTEN TO QUESTIONS THAN TO answer them. But the art of listening demands more sympathy, more humility, than we are ready to give it. To listen with full intent, with full openness, with a genuine desire to understand not the question only but the question behind the question and to be at one with the questioner—this is an engagement very difficult.

Drew Clarke was in tonight on his way home from a lecture by one of his idols, a man with a reputation for fearless thinking and courageous action. "What was he like?" I inquired.

"Grand, as usual," he said. "I've heard him now a dozen times, and he is the only churchman, present company always excepted, who has something to say. And yet tonight during the question period that followed the lecture I confess to a slight feeling of uneasiness. Was there, I wondered treasonably, something a little glib, a little mechanical, a little too easy and masterful, about his answers? Several of the questions he brushed aside or treated almost flippantly, but when he met a question that he could obviously answer, for which he had a complete solution, he perked up visibly. 'That's a good question. I'm very glad you asked that,' he said and then launched forth on an exposition that he had to my certain knowledge given a dozen times before. For the first time the unworthy suspicion crossed my mind that a good question for the doctor was a question to which he already had the answer. I missed what, adopting the fashionable phraseology, I might call an existential grappling with the question. I felt that there was no fresh thinking being done on the spot or, what is much more important, that he was not taking the questioner seriously, as opposed to taking the question seriously. Do you know what I mean?"

I think I do, for I have often been guilty of it myself.

I remember an occasion when I first became aware of the difference between answering a question and answering the questioner, and of the immorality of giving snap answers, verbal answers, answers that cost nothing in imaginative sympathy and full involvement. The Youth Group had organized a Brains Trust, to the panel of which they had invited a theologian, a preacher, and a teacher. One of the questions came from a young girl in the audience. It was the hoary old question about the problem of suffering. She asked in a quavering, uncertain voice, in which there was a hint of rebellion, why a good God should permit such awful things to happen to his children. The theologian in the group gave the most brilliant answer to that question that I have ever heard. With great passion and with a wealth of illustration he defended God; he showed the poor girl how stupid she really was to frame the question in those terms. He did everything except answer the question the girl was asking! That is, he showed no sign that he had sided with the girl in her difficulty or that he had heard the undertones of personal suffering that accompanied the question. To him it was an academic question, to her deeply personal.

Ever since that painful experience, I have tried to avoid giving glib and mechanical answers to living questions. I have tried, and I do not pretend that this is easy, to be involved with the questioner, to face the question as though it were being asked for the first time, to live with it, if only for a few seconds, to feel the full impact of it upon my own life. And this endeavor, in which I am never successful, has made me realize with new force the silence of Jesus in the Gospels and the apparent irrelevance of some of the answers he volunteered to those who came to him. So often he was answering not the question that was framed in words but the unspoken question behind it, or the question that should have been asked and wasn't. So often his silence was the measure of his deep understanding, and his full involvement in the problem that had been posed was, in fact, the only adequate answer that could be given in the circumstances.

49

I WISH THERE WERE A BOOK ON PROTESTANTISM WRITTEN FOR
the intelligent layman. I do not mean another history of Protestantism. I know there are plenty of works setting forth the origin
and growth of the denominations and sects, ranging from T. M.
Lindsay's *History of the Reformation* to John S. Whale's *The
Protestant Tradition.*

Neither do I mean a book outlining the distinctive doctrines of
Protestantism, though there is always room for an up-to-date
interpretation of the ideas behind such shop-soiled slogans as
"Justification by Faith," "The Priesthood of All Believers,"
and "The Freedom of the Christian Man." No man in our time
has done more than Paul Tillich to grasp anew these distinctive
ideas and to show their relevance for modern life. If only his
writings had the common touch!

The book I am seeking would be neither a history nor an exposition of doctrine. It would fall into two parts. First, an
exposition of Protestantism as an attitude to life. Protestantism is
not simply a religious standpoint; it is a total view of life, a way
of looking at all things and of handling all life's experiences.
Roughly speaking, it is the attitude of openness as opposed to the
desire for finality and a closed system, an expectation that truth
will be discovered on the journey. The essential Protestant, no
matter what denominational label he wears, is the man who believes that religion is a living and developing encounter with a
Person, a disturbing and never-ending encounter, not the possession of information about God. I doubt whether John Keats was a
churchgoer, but the fundamental Protestant attitude has seldom
been better expressed than in a sentence he wrote to his brother

Thomas in 1817. In the course of a discussion on the nature of the poetic genius he breaks off to say: "It struck me what quality went to form a Man of Achievement, especially in Literature, and which Shakespeare possessed so enormously—I mean NEGATIVE CAPABILITY, that is, when a man is capable of being in uncertainties, mysteries, doubts, without any irritable reaching after fact and reason."

The typical Protestant does not merely endure, he rejoices in, the growing stages of life, the frontier positions. Not only in theology, but in social and personal life, he realizes that there are no finalities. He meets people with openness, in the expectation that they will disturb and challenge his caked-up ideas, that they will upset his very human, lazy tendency to be content with slogans and labels. A modern poet, W. H. Auden, has given expression to this essentially Protestant attitude in *For the Time Being,* where he makes the Wise Men at the manger announce their discovery:

> Love does not fear substantial anarchy,
> But vividly expresses obligation
> With movement and in spontaneity.

The second part of the book would deal with what I think is an entirely neglected subject—the kind of structure necessary if our church life is to embody and express the Protestant attitude. At present, it seems to me, we are working with a structure that is a hang-over from Roman Catholicism, and the result is that our distinctive attitude to life is not given the opportunity to declare itself or to develop.

Where, for example, in our Protestant churches does the priesthood of all believers find expression? What opportunities are there during our Sunday worship for the man in the pew to exercise that priesthood? The conduct of the service is in the hands of the minister, and the worshipers are as much spectators as are Roman Catholics at Mass. In practice the priesthood of the believer means little more than that he is free to accept or reject or to pass judgment on what is said from the pulpit. He has had no hand in framing it or in co-operating with the man in the pulpit in the choice and development of the theme. As I see it, the priesthood of all believers means a shared ministry, a mutual ministry, as full a participation as possible. At present almost the only area in which this shared ministry takes effect is on the musical side of the service. A body of people willingly comes together once a week for choir practice, to do something on behalf of the whole congregation. In a fully Protestant church I envisage groups of people, summoned or voluntary, gathering with the minister in order to confer with him on the choice of sermon subjects and their development. The minister alone, however well acquainted he is with his people, cannot possibly know whether his preaching is meeting the needs of his people, cannot possibly know what problems and difficulties he is ignoring, and is not always the best judge of the full effectiveness of his presentation.

When we try to work out a Protestant structure, we shall become aware, I think, that at present we are falling between two stools. We cannot make up our minds whether to work within the tradition of the temple or in that of the synagogue. At one moment we are temple Christians, endeavoring to hold dignified services in which the elements of awe and reverence are conspicuous. At the next we are mindful of the synagogue, with its atmosphere of intimacy and informal participation, its emphasis on fellowship and teaching and sharing.

As I see it, the minister's task in a truly Protestant church is to involve the greatest number of people in the greatest number

123

of decisions, really spiritual decisions. We think we have done wonders at present when we have persuaded a few menfolk to act as sidesmen, to take up the collection, to perform sundry clerical and administrative jobs. If the priesthood of all believers is to be more than a pious phrase, we must provide the opportunities, both during the Sunday services and in other ways, for the fullest possible participation by the laity.

50

IN THE SIXPENNY BOX OUTSIDE A SECONDHAND BOOKSHOP RE-cently I picked up two little books about preachers. I have been dipping into them and am amazed at the candor and almost brutal frankness with which writers treated the idols of the pulpit thirty or forty years ago. We tend to think of our grandfathers as much less outspoken than we are, but an examination of these two volumes shows that the age of penetrating and scathing criticism of public figures has died out.

The first, *Voices of To-day,* published in 1912, is subtitled "Studies of Representative Modern Preachers." The author, Hugh Sinclair, puts some forty-six pulpit giants from a variety of denominations through as grueling an examination as I have ever read. I do not believe any contemporary religious journal would allow them to appear. There would be a tremendous outcry from softhearted readers. Too many feelings would be hurt. The mediocrity of modern religious journalism is due to this lack of frankness. Everything has to be successful, to be smothered in empty compliments. What cannot be praised is passed over in silence.

Writing of a Scottish preacher, well known in his time for work among students in Edinburgh, Hugh Sinclair says:

He believes that "the quivering heart of Christianity is found in the Cross of Christ"; he has scarcely got to the heart of that Cross. It may be that his logical bent does not give the "blazing scandal and indiscretion of it" a full chance with him. To put a frank edge on it, he is too perilously adequate to his audience. That audience certainly brings out his present best; whether it does not bar out his future possible best is an open question. One rather thinks that in a few years, face to face with a congregation whose experience he cannot quite understand, and with whose needs he cannot cope, would prove an entrance into life more abundant and evoke a sermon he has never yet preached.

The other author, "A Gentleman with a Duster," is equally frank in his *Painted Windows,* published ten years later. Speaking of the revered and saintly Bishop Gore, he writes:

From the day of the great sermons in Westminster Abbey that wonderful influence has diminished, and he is now in the unhappy position of a party leader whose followers begin to question his wisdom. Organisation has destroyed him. [He] has achieved strength at the centre of his being only at the terrible cost of cutting off, or at any rate of maiming, his own natural temperament. . . . Posterity, I think, will regretfully number him among bigots.

Concerning Dr. W. E. Orchard he is even more scathing:

Dr. Orchard does not create; he copies. His innovations are all made after visits to the lumber-room. . . . He presents the spectacle of a sparrow stretching its wings and opening its beak to imitate the eagle of catholic lecterns.

I have no idea who "A Gentleman with a Duster" was, but I have since learned that "Hugh Sinclair" is a pseudonym for Mrs. E. Herman, whose writings on mysticism are a permanent contribution to the church. *Creative Prayer* and *The Meaning and Value of Mysticism* are scholarly works, not the outpourings of a clever journalist.

What strikes me as remarkable is that Mrs. Herman, a considerable scholar in her own right and a busy person, should have taken preachers and preaching so seriously as to write this book, which entailed much time spent in reading sermons and journeying to churches all over the British Isles. She evidently believed in preaching and wished to see it better done. I just cannot imagine anyone with her gifts, capable of writing her books, doing this today. Our scholars are rather inclined to be contemptuous of us preachers, and many of those who run our theological colleges and produce our religious journals have so small an opinion of preaching that they do not even attend church except when they are preaching.

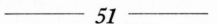

51

IT MAY BE A DEFECT IN MY MAKE-UP, BUT I CONFESS TO FINDING very little help in the mystics. A saying like Jacob Boehme's,

"Seek for the fountain of light in the deep ground of thy soul," conveys almost nothing to me. It is not when I sink down within myself that I find light, but in the give and take of personal encounter. I am most aware of God and of myself, not when I am alone, but when I am in fellowship with others. This self-awareness is very different from being self-conscious—a condition from which middle age has mercifully released me. Surely among the blessings of advancing years is that one no longer strives to make an impression, is not worried about what people think, is less afraid of making a fool of oneself in public by the expression of an honest thought, however callow or unorthodox.

I am an altogether better man when I am in company than when I am alone. I am more honest with myself, for one thing, for the presence of other people challenges me to be myself. Indeed, they give me the power of being myself, of being who I really am. Perhaps there are people who are most genuinely themselves when they are in solitude, when they are not under the necessity of giving an account of themselves to others. I can only say that it is not so with me; I am least myself, most unreal and most prone to self-deception, when I am alone.

It is only in the presence of other people that I enter into possession of my own thoughts, that I become aware of what my real convictions are. I know well what the proverb means which says, "Iron sharpeneth iron; so a man sharpeneth the countenance of his friend." How often has my own vague, groping thought been crystallized while listening to another point of view. Either I have said, "Yes, that is exactly what I think, only I could not have put it just like that," or even, "Yes, that is exactly what I think, but I was not aware of thinking it until now"; or else, conversely, "Well, whatever else I believe, I do not believe *that.*"

I think I understand Jean-Paul Sartre's famous sentence "Hell —that's other people," for I too have felt, as we all must, the threat of meeting, the insecurity into which we are sometimes thrown in the presence of others. Every person with whom I have a genuine encounter—as opposed to that glancing, mechanical thing called a "contact"—puts a question mark to my life. He forces me, if the meeting is a real one, to come out from behind my defenses to declare myself; he challenges me to emerge from the hazy, lazy world of half-formed opinions, to make the effort to articulate myself; every meeting challenges my sincerity, pulls me out of the comfortable world of ready-made ideas, slogans, labels, where I am sure of myself, into the melting pot.

But although this is uncomfortable, I do not agree with Sartre that it is "hell." It may be purgatory for a time, but it is the path to better things. Every real meeting is also an enrichment and enlargement of my life. If it didn't sound so pretentious, I would say that it "produces" my life, as taking part in a play produces the character. The part that I play in company has more reality than the part I play alone. And the richer the company, the richer the part. As M. V. C. Jeffreys, the educationalist, has said, "The plays of Shakespeare not only give the great actor his supreme opportunity and his supreme test; they also redeem the bad actor, whereas the slick plays of some modern authors only damn the bad actor."

The only mysticism I believe in is the type of mysticism I find in the apostle Paul, who has nothing to say about sinking down into the deep ground of being within, but much to say about encountering the person of the living Christ and more than is acknowledged about finding God in real personal relations. For Paul the Christian life is a drama in which one "lives with Christ," "dies with Christ," and "rises with Christ," in which one's small life is enormously enriched by getting into the play.

——— *52* ———

WHEN I CONSIDER WHAT HAS CONTRIBUTED MOST TO MY UNDER-standing of Jesus Christ apart from my own experience of his grace and fellowship, I find to my surprise that it is not what is technically known as theology. I am indebted, and grateful, of course to the professional theologians. I have even had some help from the commentators, though I sympathize with William Robertson Nicoll when he says, "In the morning I can brace my-self to most things—can and do even read commentaries on the Bible—books which often show the human intellect at its very lowest."

It is not even, as I should have expected, the poets to whom I am most indebted, but to an odd assortment of people like Nietzsche, Dostoevski, and coming to our own time, to people like Patrick Geddes and Frank Lloyd Wright. What all these people have in common is that they are real persons; what I owe to them is not so much a matter of direct insight into the meaning and message of Jesus, to what they say about him, but that they have me aware of the kind of things that Jesus was after, they have sharpened the questions to which he is the answer.

So many of the people who set out to expound and interpret the personality of Jesus seem to me to be concerned with words only, seem to diminish him to their own small size, because they have an insufficient awareness of the real problems of life. I recall the saying of Kierkegaard: "Preparation for becoming attentive to Christianity does not consist in reading many books but in deeper immersion in existence." The men to whom I refer have wrestled more profoundly with the issues of life; their diagnosis of man's condition and of the deeper movements of the age is shaped in more adequate awareness of modern experience.

So though I do not recall a single direct word from either Patrick Geddes or Frank Lloyd Wright on the subject of Jesus, from their writings I turn to him with a new appreciation of the significance of his life. These two men, who have nothing in common except an enormous zest for living and an implacable hatred of all that is rigid, mechanical, and conventional, the one a Scottish biologist, the other an American architect, awaken in me the concerns for which Jesus has the answer. His life stands out in meaningful, bold relief against the issues to which they have directed my mind.

Both these men are private discoveries of mine. No one, least of all a theological tutor, directed my attention to them, and to this day I have never heard a reference to them from any theologian of my acquaintance. Although I have called one an architect and the other a biologist, these are only convenient labels, which do but scant justice to either of them. Both had an enormous curiosity about life; both were creative to the very finger tips; both were philosophers in the old sense of thinking things together. And curiously, the architect had a biological, living approach to life and building, while the biologist is perhaps best known as a pioneer, visionary town and city planner.

ALL DAY LONG A SENTENCE FROM A MODERN POET HAS BEEN echoing in my mind. "I gave the moral answer and I died." That line seems to me to sum up the trouble with the Christian religion as practiced by most of its adherents. Christian behavior has become a matter of possessing strong moral standards, tenaciously adhered to. And these rigid moral standards cut us off from reality. Armed with them we are no longer capable of seeing things as they really are; we see everything at secondhand through the spectacles of moral judgments. Incased within this armor-plated moral system, we no longer come into living contact with people. And they on their part instinctively feel that we are not interested in them, that we have made up our minds about them, that they will get no real answers from us but only the answers dictated by our morality.

The gulf between the man in the street and the man in the pew is not a gulf created by holiness. It we were saints, the man in the street would not be suspicious, would not be frightened by us. It is not goodness that alienates the nonchurchgoer; it is unimaginative goodness, the goodness that deals in stereotypes and labels. When, in Richard Eberhart's words, we give the moral answer, something does indeed die within us and between us. Christianity cannot be adequately described in ethical terms, however richly it issues in ethical directions. It is primarily a relationship to God resulting in freedom from slavery, in a creative, spontaneous attitude to life and people.

The attempt to turn the teaching of Jesus into an ethical code, to translate the Sermon on the Mount into a new set of rules and regulations, can be successful only if the message of Jesus is torn out of its context in the kingdom of God. Christianity, as I see it, is first and foremost the response to Christ's invitation to live in the Kingdom; from within that Kingdom there can be no moral answers, only imaginative and loving living.

———— *54* ————

THE BOOKS ON MY STUDY TABLE AT THE PRESENT MOMENT ARE nearly all concerned with the parables of Jesus. I am getting ready to preach a course of sermons. In my present pastorate I have already preached two series of sermons on the parables, but I have by no means covered them all. Indeed, one reason for consulting the books is to check on the parables that I have not yet expounded; another is to give me confidence in treating them in my own way! In preaching there is no substitute for one's own fresh and original thinking. The only way to preach on the parables, or any other part of the New Testament, is to read the Book for oneself. Commentaries and other people's expositions are useful to prevent obvious howlers. They should be read *after,* not *before,* one has got down one's own work on paper.

It might be interesting to fellow craftsmen to know the titles of the books I have collected. I list them in order of usefulness. There is, of course, the classic one, Trench's *Notes on the Parables,* an old book but still very serviceable. Then C. H. Dodd's *The Parables of the Kingdom,* George Buttrick's *The Parables of Jesus,* William Barclay's *And Jesus Said,* Alexander Findlay's

Jesus and His Parables, Leslie Weatherhead's *In Quest of a King-dom,* and R. E. Roberts' *The Message of the Parables.* In addition to these, of course, there are the commentaries on the Gospels.

There they are, then, full of information and application, and there would be nothing easier than to read them and make a pot-pourri—a historical detail from Barclay, a new insight by Weath-erhead, a pertinent application to modern conditions by Roberts. But nothing from a preacher's point of view could be duller or more soul-destroying. My advice to would-be preachers is: Leave them all alone until you have read the parables for yourself, have brooded over them, have put questions to them, have taken them up the High Street for an airing. When you have done this, take a sheet of paper and jot down, not bothering to stay for any order or scheme as yet, whatever thoughts occur to you. The trouble with young preachers is that they have too little confidence in their own insights; it has been drummed into them in theological col-leges that they must be scrupulously honest with the text, and this they tend to interpret in a leaden, unimaginative way. But let them have the courage of their own insights; let them plunge directly into the heart of the parable instead of being overcon-cerned with local color and Palestinian customs!

The series of sermons on which I am at present working arose out of reading afresh those parables in which Jesus presents two characters, two types, such as the Pharisee and the publican, the man who built his house on sand and the man who built his house on rock, the prodigal son and the elder brother, the wise virgins and the foolish virgins. The longer I studied these stories, the more I was convinced that Jesus did not fully approve of either of the people he presents in contrast. In fact, the real hero of these stories never appears; he is a figure in the background, to be inferred. It struck me as inconceivable that, to take the most obvious instance, Jesus would approve and ask his hearers to emulate the careful "wise" virgins. Certainly they were "better" than the foolish maidens who fell asleep over their fast-emptying lamps, but their unwillingness to share their oil with their silly sisters was most unchristian. In the same way, I asked myself, is the real alternative to praying within oneself in self-righteous congratulation like the Pharisee in the temple, praying in groveling, self-despising "humility," like the publican? Is either of these attitudes really Christian? And so also with the two builders. It is obviously more sensible to build on rock than on sand, but elsewhere in the Gospels I do not find much approval for people who seek security and finality. There is a "rockiness" that prevents living encounter with God, a false security, a premature finality that is the death of that ever-renewed fellowship with God that is the heart of Christ's religion. The proper foundation for the house of life is the living soil, neither rock nor sand, but the good earth.

55

WHAT ARE "RELIGIOUS" BOOKS? SEVERAL MEMBERS OF MY congregation have told me recently, obviously angling for my approval, that they have been reading, and actually enjoying, the novels of Lloyd Douglas and the works of Norman Vincent Peale. They have surprised themselves, and obviously wish it to be counted unto them for righteousness, by finding *The Robe* and *The Big Fisherman* both interesting and informative. It puts me in an awkward position when they ask what I think of these volumes, for the honest answer is that I consider them unreadable. If I say frankly that I consider them dull and uninspired, written in clichés and journalese, deficient in penetrating religious judgment, it sounds as though I am discouraging their newly awakened interest in "good" books.

If I go further and say that I find more real religion in writers like William Faulkner and Joyce Cary, or John Steinbeck and Graham Greene, they are apt to be scandalized, for these are not good books about good people. There is little here that bears the obvious label "religious." There is much in both the language and the situations that offends the conventional churchgoer. How can I explain that a "religious" book is not necessarily a book that reconstructs a New Testament incident, or that depicts the ultimate triumph of the right, or that avoids the presentation of unpleasant people. A "religious" book is the result of a religious attitude to life; it is the product of deep compassion, of a fundamental seriousness about the reality of good and evil, about the depth and power of evil. It is a book that takes seriously the human predicament, that does not gloss over what is ugly and malign and misshapen. It is informed and suffused with a great pity for man in his plight; it sees man, not men; the individual in his solitariness, not types or stock characters. It may not use religious terminology or quote the words of Jesus, but it stands where he stood, for all that is living, spontaneous, and free against all that is dead, mechanical, and necessitated. A religious book, no matter how sordid its characters or how foul its language, is a prayer of wrath and a plea for pity.

A man might rise from reading such books as *The Robe* and *The Big Fisherman* with a sense of satisfaction that at last he, the least pious of men, has actually finished and indeed enjoyed

135

a religious book; he might congratulate himself that he has improved his knowledge of the historical background and added to his stock of information about Eastern customs and primitive religious ritual and belief, that he now knows more about the towering personalities of Jesus and Paul. But if he confines himself to such books, he will have little idea of the depth and power of these personalities. For one thing, the range and rage of the demonic escapes the author; he writes in insufficient awareness of the insidious, gripping stranglehold of sin. For another, he is not poet enough or mystic enough to portray the essential character of Jesus or Paul, and the very flatness and woodenness of his reconstruction of the speech and deeds of these men actually distorts and diminishes them. The style of an author is a better clue to his understanding of a religious genius than any amount of religious information. As the young Negro teacher Nathan Scott, Jr., has said:

A writer's explicit creedal statements are the least reliable register of his actual beliefs, which are usually conveyed through his technique, through whatever form it is that he imposes upon the crude stuff of experience. The way in which a writer brings the resources of language into the service of his subject is the measure not only of his importance as an artist but also of the values by which he is sustained as both artist and human being.

The Irish poet AE has expressed the same thought with more moving power: "No Church today can convince me that it is inspired until the words arising from it even in anger break in a storm of beauty on the ear."

56

THE YOUNG MAN IN MY STUDY TONIGHT WAS AGGRESSIVELY antichurch. He made it quite clear that he was only there under pressure. His bride to be is a member of my church and had brought him along to discuss arrangements for the wedding ceremony. But when the details had been fixed up, he thawed a little, and while I was out of the room making a cup of tea, he had evidently been inspecting my shelves, for when I returned, he wanted to know, "How is it that you, a Protestant minister, and if Mary's reports of your sermons are true, a very convinced Protestant, have so many books by Roman Catholic authors on your shelves?" Like many other young men, especially if they have Left-wing political sympathies, he evidently supposed that I was not allowed to read outside the party line! I meet this idea again and again among people who are unfamiliar with church life; they assume that we ministers are unable to entertain any point of view not approved by our denomination. And then it occurred to him that I had an ulterior motive. "I suppose that you like to keep informed as to what the enemy is doing."

When he had gone, I trust a sadder and a wiser man, I took stock of the books now on my study table, and I surprised myself by finding so many Roman Catholic authors facing me. Cheek by jowl with Kenneth Hamilton's *The Protestant Way* was Father Victor White's *God the Unknown,* and next to William Neil's *The Plain Man Looks at the Bible* was Emmanuel Mounier's *The Spoil of the Violent.* Alongside these were Gabriel Marcel's *The Mystery of Being* and Jacques Maritain's *Creative Intuition*—two Protestants to four Catholics! And I think how much poorer my intellectual and spiritual life would be had I never made the acquaintance of my fellow Christians in the Roman fold, had I confined myself to writers with whom I wholeheartedly agree or to the works of a particular school.

My understanding of the pastoral office has been immeasurably enriched by the wisdom of Bishop Heenan's *The People's Priest* and by Baron von Hügel's *Letters to a Niece*. I am deeply grateful for the light that has been shed upon man in the modern world by such people as Gustave Thibon, Mounier, Eric Gill, and Gerald Vann. I should be sociologically illiterate had I never met these and other Roman Catholic writers. Fundamentally as we differ on many points of theology, I recognize this merit in Roman Catholic sociological thought—it is not the hand-to-mouth, frequently sentimental, haphazard thought that so often characterizes Protestant pronouncements; it proceeds logically and inevitably from first principles. Needless to say, I am talking about Roman Catholic theory and not Roman Catholic practice. Roman Catholic writers are the first to admit and deplore the fact that the faithful pay so little heed to the papal encyclicals on social and economic questions.

Naturally I do not go to Roman Catholic writers for biblical exegesis (although their exposition is frequently enlightening) or for church history, but I see no reason why I should deprive myself or my congregation of the insights and help that come from devout men of God, nurtured in an ancient tradition, when they are speaking of the ways of God with the human soul, or discussing the devout life, or bringing their critical sense to bear upon modern psychology. I can discard much in the writings of men like Léon Bloy, Charles Péguy, Jacques Maritain and Raïssa, his wife, Pierre Emmanuel, and still find food for thought, aye, and food for the soul. And it is my growing conviction that the deeper we both go into our distinctive faiths, the nearer we come to each

138

other. The most serious points of disagreement are often between bad Catholics and bad Protestants, each shouting to cover up a bad conscience.

57

THREE OR FOUR TIMES A YEAR I AM ASKED TO TAKE RELIGIOUS services in government offices or on business premises. This week I have slogged out every morning to the Department of Agriculture, where each day before the work of the day officially begins, I conduct a short prayer and Bible service for the Christian Union. Next month I shall be doing the same during the lunch hour at the office of National Insurance. Few people realize that this sort of thing is going on up and down the country. Even my own church members have no idea of the calls that are made upon my time in this way.

I accept these invitations gladly. The numbers are very small. This morning in a building where four hundred people work there were seven people at the service. I tell myself that numbers do not matter. It is a good thing that there are 7 people leavening the lump, preparing the atmosphere in which their 393 colleagues will spend the rest of the day. The calls upon the patience and understanding of public officials are many; it is grand that the interviews and contacts will be carried through in a spirit of prayer.

I should feel more convinced by my own argument if the people in the group did not look so smug! But I am sure that I should look and feel smug if I had risen twenty minutes earlier than was necessary. They are all regular and devout members of churches and chapels, mostly it must be admitted of the Baptist persuasion and given to a literal interpretation of the Bible. Why is it that evangelical fundamentalists are so much keener on public witness than their more liberal friends? The answer they would give is that they have got hold of the right end of the stick, but I wonder if there is not some relation between a rather mechanically conceived faith and a rigid pattern of witness. However that may be, the fact remains that they remain a small group and often wonder why their professedly Christian colleagues do not join them. It so happens that three of my own best members work in this particular office, and not even to support me would they be seen dead in the prayer group! For one thing, they shrink from setting up another division within the working life of the office. For the same reason that they dislike wearing badges, they dislike cutting themselves off from their fellow men or making normal, man-to-man conversation more difficult. But the deeper reason is that they are genuinely devout Christians, too; only they place more stress on the witness of comradeship, conscientious workmanship, helpful personal relations, than on the public practice of prayer. When Whittaker Chambers turned from Communism to become a Christian, he was still on the staff of *Time* magazine.

Now a truly wonderful thing began to happen to me. I do not know what force moved the gravitation, but little by little people began to open my office door at *Time* which in my own need few had ever opened. They would sit down and after a rambling preamble, suddenly confide to me some distress that was destroying their peace or their lives. . . . I never spoke of religion to these sufferers unless I was specifically asked about it, and then reluctantly and little.

Perhaps I will quote this passage tomorrow morning; I may not be asked back again!

58

Fairbrother tried to stir up the ministers' fraternal
today by declaring that every Roman Catholic doctrine repudiated
by the Reformers has crept back into Protestantism by the back
door. What we have dismissed as a theological principle, we have
readmitted as a secular one. He instanced Luther's passionate
affirmation of justification by faith alone. This was a counterblast
to the Roman Catholic doctrine of justification by works, to the
idea that man can win divine approval by his good deeds. The
Protestant man of today believes theoretically in justification by
faith, but his practice is based on justification by work, by hard
work, by overwork. He is a hard worker on principle, although
he does not realize what the principle is! He may think that it is
the other Lutheran doctrine of vocation that thus drives him to
work hard for the glory of God, but even when he has lost his
religion, the Protestant still works hard, driven by an unconscious
urge to justify himself, if not in God's eyes, then in his own. It is
his guilty conscience that leads him to take home a laden brief
case from the office every night. Fairbrother produced Thomas
Carlyle and Arthur Koestler as examples of this thesis. When the
Calvinistic Scot lost his religion, he reaffirmed his natural catholicism; he embraced the religion of work. His strident proclama-
tion of the gospel of work is almost neurotic. Similarly Koestler,
the Hungarian Jew without a faith, finds consolation, as did
Freud, in tremendous bouts of labor. Koestler admits as much
in his autobiography, *The Invisible Writing:*

Gradually these maniacal bursts of activity, followed by morbid
depressions, levelled out into a relatively stable working discipline

which keeps me chained to my desk all the year round for eight or nine hours a day. For an independent writer this is an unusual routine, and the chains are self-imposed; but each time I have tried to break them I had to pay the penalty of being relegated into a limbo of maudlin drunkenness, tormenting hangovers, and phantom Helenas. Thus Work became my therapy and drug, my compromise with a guilt-ridden ego, and a sacrificial offering to the ghosts of the past . . . an atonement for an unknown original sin.

Fairbrother might have brought in John Ruskin as another witness. Did he not say that no monk in a cell, denying and flagellating himself, imposed half so tyrannical a routine upon himself as the modern businessman who was prepared to lead an austere, starved inner life for the sake of business?

59

THE BEST ADVICE I EVER RECEIVED WAS: SELL YOURSELF IN THE highest market! It came from the successful pastor of a flourishing seaside church. I had gone to consult him about a possible move from the suburbs to the slums. For many months I had been nagged by a feeling that I had advantages that were not being fully exploited in my pleasant suburban pastorate. I was young, unmarried, and unencumbered by domestic responsibilities, and I was doing a job that could be done equally well, perhaps better, by a married man with a growing family to provide for. There was a church in the East End of London, a vast cavernous Victorian building, attended by a sparse handful of faithful people who were quite unable to "call" a minister, since they had no funds available to pay his salary. The situation was so desperate that the church was on the point of closing its doors, though all around there swirled a teeming population. Would I not be better occupied throwing my youthful energies into this lost cause than in looking after a hundred or so comfortable suburban families? I could live on practically nothing; I could devote my whole time to the job, undistracted by family cares. "You're being romantic," said the great man. "Let me give you some advice, born of long experience. People are apt to take you at your own valuation. Do something for nothing, and they will value it accordingly. You have only one life to live; spend it where it will be likely to bring you most profit." And then came the words, "Sell yourself in the highest market." I'm afraid that he was thinking in terms of salary and prestige, but the words clinched the indecision of months. Of course he was right! I had only one life to live, and it would be a thousand pities to waste it by doing a job anyone else could do, a job which did not fully stretch me. The result was that I spent the next six years of my life being absurdly happy, rich in friends and experience. Even financially the pressure did not last long. By scraping together every available penny, that little congregation paid me three pounds a week to begin with, and I never lacked for anything. But very soon that sum was increased, thanks to the interference of the London Transport Board! The extension of the Underground Railway into Essex necessitated the local undertaker finding new premises. He built his temporary showroom on our ample forecourt, which brought us an income of another three pounds a week without making any difference to the amenities of the church. The East Ender is realistic enough to see no incon-

143

gruity in associating the undertaker with the parson! I look back on those years among the cheerful cockneys of Bethnal Green as among the best years, the most richly rewarding years, of my life.

After twenty-three years in the ministry I can see that there has been a wonderfully variegated pattern in my life. First, three years in the suburbs, making the mistakes of immaturity among a people much too polite and kind to object. Then six years in the East End, years filled with alarm and tragedy, for I shared with my people the first air raids on London. Then on the invitation of the denomination nine years in charge of a highly organized central mission in the historic borough of Southwark, where Chaucer and Dickens met one at every turn. And finally for the last few years pastor in a university city ministering to a mixed congregation of workers, professional men, and students.

I am sometimes asked, Where did you think your best work was done? Which type of congregation took the most out of you? Where were you most usefully employed—in the suburb, the slum, or the city? I find that question most difficult to answer. When I was younger, I was convinced that I was wasting my time in the suburbs; it seemed to me that suburban people had so many advantages, lovely homes, varied interests, executive jobs that demanded responsibility, troops of friends, that there was no great place for the church in their lives. In striking contrast the men and women with unsatisfactory homes, crowded conditions, humdrum jobs, a hand-to-mouth existence, needed the ministry of the church far more. But this, I now see, was a mistake. In many ways it is harder to minister to suburban people. Their needs are just as great, but it is more difficult to get at them. The Cockney, for instance, has very few of the middle-class inhibitions, reserves, tight-lipped secrecies, of the suburbanite. He will unburden his heart more freely; you waste no time beating about the bush; he is almost embarrassingly frank. One has to win the confidence of the man and woman in the suburbs by patient and very understanding identification. Besides which, the dweller in suburbia is much more self-aware than his brother in slumdom; he senses patronage more easily; he suspects interference and exploitation. The effort to get into the heart of a suburban family demands patience and real humility. It is notoriously easier to serve people who obviously need your help than people who stand in no obvious need of it. That is why one comes across ministers who are "good with young people," "good with poor people," who cut no ice with their co-equals or their social and economic superiors.

60

SHORT CUTS ARE AS RISKY IN RELIGION AS IN HIKING—BUT NOT nearly so harmless. I have just spent three hours with a young fellow who was "soundly converted" in an evangelistic rally some months ago. Now that the emotional excitement has died down, he is back where he began, indeed further back. The glow has faded, and he is feeling distressed because he has fallen down on his conversion, broken his vows, dishonored Christ. And mingling with this self-accusation there is an uneasy suspicion that he had allowed himself to be taken in by methods of mass exploitation. Either way he blames himself.

As we talked together, it became obvious to me that here was a case of a young man accepting a premature solution to a problem that had not been sufficiently explored. Like many thousands of his kind, he had been aware of moral lapses, mainly of a sexual nature. The preacher's call to acknowledge and renounce his sins had found a ready response; the unspecified "sins" were identified in his mind with the temptations he shared with thousands of other normal young people. It was at this point that he met Christ. In other words, he accepted Christ as the solution of his sex problem. He came to terms with him on too narrow a front; he "accepted Christ" at the point of his failure and weakness rather than of his strength and goodness. But the obvious place at which a man feels his alienation from God is not necessarily the real one. A man's "sins" are often only the symptoms of a more secret, radical, and unconfessed estrangement. Of course he had experienced a temporary, and real, feeling of adequacy; his life as a result of this decision had been pulled together—for the moment. He had sung and quite sincerely: " 'Tis done, the great transaction's done," but it was a transaction at a superficial level. It did not last. How could it? It was not the whole man who had committed itself to Christ, but that part of him which stood in obvious and pressing need. There had been no attempt to probe the matter further, to discover what wrong attitude to life, what immature feelings, what unsatisfactory relationships, had sought relief or compensatory expression in the "sins" he had committed.

This young man was humble enough to think that there might be something in what I said, and before he left tonight very quietly and without fuss, he had committed himself, as well as his "sins," to Christ. I read to him Gabriel Marcel's moving words concerning his conversion to the Christian faith:

I can in no sense boast of having *arrived*. I am convinced that I see more clearly than I did, though "convinced" is a word at once too weak and too intellectual. Perhaps it would be better to say this: the freer and more detached parts of me have struggled up into the light, but there is still much of me that lies in shadow, untouched by the almost level rays of the dawning sun; much of me is still, as Claudel would put it, unevangelised.

It is an unexamined assumption of evangelism that one should preach so as to produce a conviction of sin and that without this conviction nothing further is possible. I for one should like to see that assumption questioned. Nothing is easier than to produce a conviction of sin in full-blooded young people at a certain level, and the very ease with which this is done should make it suspect. Some of the best and most lasting conversions have been those of people who felt no conviction of sin in this narrow sense, but were moved by the sight of the suffering of others, or longed to be of use to humanity, or felt, as Schweitzer did, that every privilege entailed a responsibility, that every blessing hid at its heart a demand.

A really adequate evangelism must stress the need for the reconciliation of the whole personality to God, not only that part of it that has gone obviously awry or stands in immediate need. Moral struggle and defeat are not the only factors in the situation. Man reveals his estrangement from God by the divorce between his reason and imagination, between his work and leisure, between body and soul, by his inadequate handling of personal relationships as well as by his moral conflicts. The evangelism that can handle man only in crisis and has no word to speak to him in his contentment and happiness is not true to the witness of the New Testament.

61

THE MAN IN THE PULPIT YESTERDAY WAS A MISSIONARY ON furlough from India, spending part of his scanty leave traveling up and down the British Isles appealing for men and money. The very sight of him there in my pulpit, an obviously overworked and devoted servant of Jesus Christ, made me ashamed of my own feeble ministry here at home. It was a benediction to sit under his preaching, and my heart warmed toward him as he prayed for the "pastor of this congregation and his work." How seldom we preachers hear ourselves commended to God!

But I wondered again, as I have wondered many times, why missionaries with few exceptions present such a poor case for the work they so obviously love and believe in. Is it partly because they underrate their audiences? They give the impression of speaking to tight-fisted shareholders who wish to know that their money has been spent to the best advantage. They believe that we are interested only in success stories, whereas our interest would be quickened and our purse strings untied if they were to share with us more frankly the difficulties they face, the frustration they feel at having to perform a hundred chores that prevent them making effective contact with men and women, the opposition they are now encountering everywhere from the quickened vitality of the great religions Buddhism, Hinduism, and Mohammedanism, to say nothing of the revival of primitive, tribal religions in fields where but a few years ago the Christian Church was making headway. To hear many missionaries speak, one would imagine that they operated in a vacuum where Christianity was the only religious and cultural force in existence.

Our guest yesterday was from India. No word passed his lips about the traditional and ancestral faith of that continent. Yet there are several people in this congregation who know a little of the writings of men like Tagore and Professor S. Radhakrishnan, and wonder what contact there is between the Christian Church and the best elements of Hinduism. They already suspect that missionaries, however personally humble and modest, are arrogant enough to believe that Christianity alone is true and that all other religions are false, that Christianity alone is right, whereas every other manifestation of the religious spirit in man is wrong. Surely the uniqueness of Christianity lies in this, not that it is a better religion than those already in the field, but that it is not a religion at all. It can therefore co-operate and rejoice in the deepening and cleansing of all religions, because it is not in competition with any. Religion is man's search for God, the sum of the techniques, the manipulation of experience and personality whereby man seeks to make contact with spiritual power. Christianity is a gospel; it is the good news that God has done something, that he has given himself to man in the person of Jesus of Nazareth. The Christian is a witness to that event and to that person. And where, as in India, that witness has been made faithfully, the effect through men like Gandhi, Tagore, Radhakrishnan, is to make Hinduism critical of itself, to purify and deepen the ancestral religion, to send men to their own scriptures with new insights to guide them in their exposition of such typically Indian doctrines as reincarnation, karma, and maya. The way in which men like Professor Radhakrishnan have expounded these doctrines has lifted them up out of fatalism and superstition and provided many common areas for conversation and co-operation.

When Jesus called upon his disciples to be the "salt of the earth," was he not calling upon his men to bring out the flavor in

149

other people, as salt brings out the flavor of food? And is this not our privilege in regard to the other great religions—so to witness among them that they might become aware of themselves in a deeper and truer way? We need not fear this, for it is our conviction that all roads lead to Christ and that it is he himself who "lighteth every man that cometh into the world."

62

NO WORD IN THE CHRISTIAN VOCABULARY NEEDS SUCH CAREFUL watching as the little word "sin." It is constantly on the preacher's tongue in both sermons and public prayers, but what does it mean? A bright lad in my congregation once suggested that I should give the word a six months' holiday. "Every time you feel the urge to use it, stop and tell us precisely what you have in mind—drunkenness, lust, envy, sharp business practice, downright laziness, or what? It would greatly add to the vividness of your sermons and to the discomfort of your congregation!"

But is it as easy as that? Like Ruskin and Blake I realize the effectiveness of "minute particulars" and that it is the preacher's temptation to slide off into vague generalities. But I am also persuaded that there is a false concreteness, a misleading precision. One of the virtues of the word "sin" in my eyes is its very lack of precision. Because it is a vague and general term, each hearer is compelled, or at least allowed, to fill the word with a content strictly applicable to him, to his stage of growth, to his private experience. The word awakens in him the response which he is capable of making at that moment in his personal history. What bothers a man at the age of twenty ought not to have the same seriousness for him when he is forty. So when I utter the word "sin" before a congregation, I know that each person present will be making his own adjustment to it according to his age, experience, sensitiveness, and insight.

I have come to think of late years that it is possible to take our "sins" too seriously. I remember the shock of recognition with which I greeted the words of the Hungarian poet Attila Jozsef, quoted by his old school friend Arthur Koestler:

> . . . lush and poisoned grasses start
> rank from my pure and simple heart.

Are there not actions to which we give way temporarily which do not in the slightest belong to our fundamental nature? Not every "sin" expresses our settled attitude to life. There is a great difference between an action, let us say getting drunk, when it is an evasion of the claims of God upon one's life, when it is done with the deliberate intention of side-stepping responsible encounter with reality, and the same action undertaken out of mere conviviality.

Besides which, the attempt to render concise and concrete the definition of "sin" ignores the fact that the same action may be a vice in one man and a virtue in another, a blameworthy act in a boy and an admirable one in a mature man. There are times in the life of a growing boy when aggressiveness is wholly right, when he would be a monster if he were humble. It is his duty to "produce" himself, not to efface himself. There are occasions when wrath is entirely justified, when self-sacrifice is timidity. I have

151

had enough pastoral experience to know that there is more danger in listing and codifying sins than there is in being vague about them.

Where we need more precision and definition is in our interpretation of sin as opposed to sins. Our sins are the local manifestations, the outcroppings, of our attitude to life; sin is that attitude when it is wrongheaded, immature, rebellious, or evasive. But to say that all sin is selfishness, or an offense against God, or a flouting of the law, is not in my view adequate; it is too moralistic, too legalistic. I prefer William Blake's assessment of sin as the refusal to be creative. "The man who is not an artist is not a Christian." Sin is being mechanical where one should be vital, being imitative where one should be original, being submissive to an external authority where one should be responsive to the ever-renewed, ever-changing voice of the living God. My own private definition of sin, whereby I measure my own actions and those of others, may not sound very theological, but I think it has the root of the matter in it. "Sin is any and every action that I perform without the full consent of my whole personality."

63

SOME WEEKS AGO AN OLD GENTLEMAN IN MY CONGREGATION PRE-sented me with a volume of sermons. He had listened to them as a young man fifty years ago, preached from my pulpit by a distinguished predecessor. (I wonder, by the way, why all predecessors are "distinguished.") There was no malice in the gift; he was drawing no comparisons; he merely wished for me to possess an interesting record of the past.

I have spent an evening reading the sermons, and I can well understand why they drew big congregations at the beginning of the century. They are written in vigorous, manly English; they are addressed to the practical problems of daily life; they are free from theological jargon. The texts are straightforward, the structure strong and bony, the illustrations are relevant, the style crisp.

But now, having laid the book down, I am trying to imagine the reception these sermons would get from a modern congregation. I think they would fall pretty flat. For one thing, they are not sufficiently theological. Modern man may dislike theological jargon, but he is increasingly aware of the futility of trying to persuade people to adopt Christian standards before they have become Christians. A great deal of preaching at the beginning of the century was aimed at inculcating Christian ideals without very much reference to the necessity for a fundamental reconstruction of personality, for a new relationship to God in Christ.

And another thing, the gospel presented in these sermons was addressed to the needs of a society that has passed away. I got the impression that the preacher was concerned to fit men to take their place in a rising capitalist society. The virtues he commended were those demanded by an economy of scarcity, namely, thrift and sobriety. The gospel was harnessed to the demands of the machine for reliable timekeepers, for hard workers undistracted by frivolous pursuits. It was a gospel of self-improvement and sanctified self-interest, narrowly conceived. This is the kind of illustration that must have gone down big with a congregation of small businessmen and ambitious workingmen:

I have five clerks in my office [said a Bradford merchant lately] who probably could tell me all I want to know and more about a horse race, a cricket or a football match; and not one of them could translate for me a foreign business letter. This is one principle reason [he added] why Bradford is over-run with Germans, and why the Germans are getting hold of so much of our trade.

To preach in this strain today would strike no sparks—not because our young people are lazy or indifferent to worldly success, but because they are living in a different kind of society and because they have come to realize that the good life involves the cultivation of leisure, the flowering of the artistic and cultural side of life as well as of business acumen and industrial reliability. It is noteworthy that J. B. Priestley was brought up in Bradford. Looking back to his boyhood he gives it as his opinion that, where it not for the presence of the German-Jewish business community, there would have been precious little musical and artistic life in that drab city. But of this the preacher said not a word.

And this led me to reflect on the nature of preaching today. Are not we also guilty of harnessing the gospel to the demands of a particular type of society, which is destined to pass away? How far, I wondered, is the moral teaching given from our pulpits in the name of Jesus of Nazareth not his at all, but an adaptation, even a subtle and unconscious perversion of his teaching, shaped to meet the needs of our mid-twentieth-century society? It is easy enough to criticize a man like Dr. Norman Vincent Peale, who has shaped his message to meet the needs of the modern American businessman, harassed and driven, caught up in the anxieties and pressures of a competitive system, but are we not all guilty in some measure of the same thing? How much of our preaching is designed to fit men into a certain kind of society which we take for granted? How much of it is designed to make men aware of

154

what that society is doing to them, to become critical of it, even to rebel against it?

So it was in a very sober mood that I handed the book back to my old friend and with questions like these ringing in my mind: If an economy of scarcity demands the virtue of thrift, what is the corresponding virtue demanded in an economy of abundance? If a predatory society demands security, does a welfare state demand excitement and variety and change? And how does the eternal gospel fare from our pulpits?

64

DON MARQUIS DECLARED THAT PUBLISHING A VOLUME OF POETRY was like dropping a rose leaf down the Grand Canyon. My resignation from the local evangelistic committee a year ago had the same devastating effect. No one took the slightest notice. They went ahead and invited Dr. Billy Graham anyway! Since then I have been under a certain amount of fire from some of my fellow ministers for refusing to play my part in "this great spiritual movement." I don't mind that, it at least gives us something to talk about when we meet, and it is good for a man that he should give reasons for the faith that is in him. My objection to Billy Graham has nothing personal in it; I am the first to admit that he is a sincere and dedicated man of God; it arises inevitably from my theological convictions. In uncharitable parenthesis it seems to me that the co-operation that some of my colleagues were willing to accord Billy was purely an *ad hoc* measure; they clutched at him like a drowning man clutching at a rope. I am stung into saying this by the accusation that is sometimes brought that I am being deliberately obstructive, playing the odd man out, and enjoying it. Well, I don't deny that I find something exhilarating in being in a minority, even in a minority of one. There is as much of the old Adam in me as in the next man. But the possibility of self-deception being granted, I still feel that my decision was sincerely and honorably taken.

Part of my objection to the message and methods of Dr. Graham, and I said this long before he came on the scene, is that he, like his theologically dissimilar colleague Dr. Norman Vincent Peale, is exploiting the spirit of the age rather than resisting it. He is meeting men at the level of their wants rather than of their needs. Again I emphasize that I believe he is doing this in absolute sincerity. Whether consciously or not, his preaching is slanted toward the cry of men and women for authority, certainty, for a simple formula, for a glamorous or successful personality, for participation in a crowd, for adjustment to a difficult and wearing environment. No one can deny that there is a dearth of personalities on the modern scene, or the appeal that successful projectors of themselves like Johnnie Ray or Liberace exercise upon the multitude. It is clear, too, that in an age of uncertainty and confusion of counsel there is magnetic power in a man who speaks without a trace of hesitation or who invokes some magic formula like "the Bible says." Modern man is lonely; the appeal of a tremendous crowd is fascinating. He is emotionally starved; the release and heightening, even if it be only temporary, of music and light and color is a powerful one. He knows he is guilty, he is defeated, he is discouraged; the offer to make a quick decision, to halt the drift, is an attractive one.

Certainly the evangelist must take men where they are. But there is a difference between meeting man at the point of his obvious and immediate wants, and eliciting his real needs. That the man of today *wants* authority, certainty, security, is undeniable. That he *needs* these things is questionable. As I see it, speaking as an unrepentant Protestant, what man needs is not authority, but the power to do without authority; not certainty and security, but the willingness to face the radical uncertainty of an encounter with the living God; not a slogan or a formula for successful living or power to adjust to his environment, but the power and courage to resist what his environment is doing to him. What man needs is not to feel good in the middle of a crowd, but to face the struggle of creating true community. What he needs is to realize himself as a person, to achieve a reconciliation not only within his moral nature, but within his total personality.

Influenced as I am by Martin Buber and the existentialists, I have come to suspect any evangelism that meets man at the point of his immediate wants. The evangelist's first task in an age like this is to make man aware of his fundamental needs, to recover man for himself. It is comparatively easy in evangelistic preaching to "exploit the psychological frustrations and privations of the industrialized masses." There is a way of uttering the words "Come to Jesus" that bypasses the fact that man, the man of today, is incapable of making a genuine response to that gracious invitation. We do him a disservice by encouraging him to believe otherwise. God is the most real being; no man can respond to him who is not willing to be real. God is the perfect person; no man can respond to him who is not willing to be personal. And personal is not private. To be deeply and truly personal is a terrific demand upon men who are accustomed to being mechanical and evasive in their relationships with one another. Again and again I return to the words of Kierkegaard, "Preparation for becoming attentive to Christianity does not consist in reading many books . . . but in fuller immersion in existence."

But I must pay this tribute to Billy Graham, if he will accept it; he has made me think out my own position, made me more aware of what it is I am trying to do, and convinced me of the fact that I am not doing it with a fraction of the power and dedication with which he is doing *his* job.

65

IT SEEMS TO BE ASSUMED THAT IF ONLY WE PREACHERS COULD make ourselves intelligible to the plain man, he would respond to our message. What alienates him is our theological jargon, our archaic vocabulary, our dog-collar words. Certainly there is a case to be made out for simplicity, but no one complained of the obscurity of Jesus. It was the devastating clarity of his message that provoked hostility. The better they understood him, the less they liked him. It was not because he was unintelligible that the men of his day hounded him to the Cross.

I am reminded of all this because I have just been listening to a very able speaker on the fashionable subject of "communication." He made great play with the words of the apostle Paul to the Corinthians, "Wherefore let him that speaketh in an unknown tongue pray that he may interpret," pointing out that the language we use in the pulpits and in church circles is just as much gibberish to the man in the street as were the ecstatic utterances of the early Church. To be sure, there was this difference, that whereas the "unknown tongues" of the first century riveted men's attention by their vehemence and strangeness, our theological jargon and pulpit voices merely put men to sleep. But this only highlights the point that the need for interpretation is more urgent and necessary than ever.

We all agreed with him that words like "sanctification," "justification," "atonement," need reminting in every generation. But is it the "hard" words that are so difficult to understand? What about the simple ones? How does one remint words like "love," "faith," "hope," "sin"? Is it the words that are the stumbling block or the ideas behind the words?

When we have done all that is humanly possible to streamline and clarify the vocabulary of the Bible, substituting perhaps psychological and scientific jargon for the old-fashioned picture words of the Bible, the ideas behind the words will still be foreign to the "natural" man, still an "offense" to him and more of an "offense" the more clearly he understands them. All our ingenuity, our command of modern idiom, our skill at restatement, will only serve to throw into still higher relief the essential strangeness of the Bible message. For the world of the Bible is an upside-down world; it is a world where men are judged before they are even tried. "All have sinned, and come short of the glory of God." It is a world where righteousness is filthy rags, where nothing is earned but all is given, where the first are last and the last are first, where, as Coleridge said, men do not repent in order that they might be forgiven, but where they are forgiven in order that they might repent.

Put this as clearly as you will, it is still gibberish to the ordinary

159

man. And we shall interpret not by adding words to words, but only by bringing about an encounter with the "Word made flesh."

66

ONE OF THE MOST INTERESTING COMMITTEES ON WHICH I AM privileged to serve is the selection board of a theological college. This morning we interviewed five candidates for the ministry. Every denomination, even the Roman Catholics, reports a shortage of man power. I suppose we ought to be surprised, in view of the paltry financial inducement and the lack of security, that we get any candidates at all. It is often said that the deeper reason for the shortage is that the best of our young people feel they can exercise their Christian vocation more profitably elsewhere than in the professional ministry. They do not consider the calling of a parson to be a big enough job. They are not persuaded that the care of a hundred or so families, which is what the job boils down to in the majority of cases, is the most rewarding and exciting use of their lives. There is truth in this, but why is it that such candidates as we do get are nearly all heading for the home ministry, ignoring the challenge and difficulty of service abroad with the missionary societies? There they would have a big enough job in all conscience—a parish as big as Wales, enough responsibility to break their backs, and a call upon every talent and skill they happen to possess from scholarship to shipbuilding!

No, there must be another reason, and as I listened to the candidates, I began to think I saw what it might be.

Each of the young men before us had been asked to submit a written statement of his faith and experience. My goodness, how theological our young people are! One of the candidates, a smooth-faced boy of eighteen with a candid look and an engaging smile, prefaced his credo with the words: "I believe in the universality of human sin." Others, somewhat more kindly disposed toward the human race, had confided to us their views on such complex subjects as providence, the virgin birth, immortality, and biblical inspiration. After a time the atmosphere got so learned and academic that I longed for one of these nice lads to break through the web of theological jargon and talk to us naturally. It would have been a change to hear one of them say, "I believe in life, and I intend by God's help to live it to the full." I would like to have heard what they believed about love, marriage, work, sport, and whether they preferred soccer to rugby and why.

But of course I was being unfair. I cast my mind back to the day when I stood in their shoes. When I got home, I dug out a copy of the statement on faith and experience that I submitted twenty-odd years ago. And of course it was just as theological! As I read it over, I couldn't recognize myself and for the very good reason that the real me wasn't in it; it was not my statement, but the statement I had been led to believe the committee would want to hear. It was a convocation of theological phrases picked up from preachers and books. For me, as I suspect for most of these lads, religion was very imperfectly related to life. At its most intense it had something to do with the moral struggle, with sin, with my efforts to grow up. God was a restraining rather than a creative power in my life. I touched him where I fell, not where I grew. And I wonder whether this isn't the real reason for the lack of candidates for the ministry, that the most perceptive and sensitive of our young people cannot envisage themselves in the role of moral policemen or as concerned with only a tiny fraction of man's total experience. They do not want to be employed in a little world wherein they will be cut off from exciting experiments in living and learning, from the arts, from the growing areas of modern man's workaday existence.

67

IF A CONGREGATION COULD GET AN X-RAY VIEW OF WHAT IS going on in the preacher's head as he stands facing them in the pulpit, wouldn't they be surprised? I am often surprised at myself. I marvel, not only at the contents, but at the variety of thoughts it is possible to entertain at one and the same time. I stand in the pulpit reading the scripture on a Sunday morning; one part of my mind is concentrated on the passage before me, another is speculating about the carrying power of my voice, yet another part is feeling faintly irritated by the girl in the choir who is turning over the pages of her hymnbook, while still another is pondering the effect this passage is likely to be having on the young man in the gallery who last night discussed with me his religious doubts. And then, quite unbidden, another thought joins this motley crowd: a remembered sentence of Emerson's, "The sense of being perfectly well-dressed gives a feeling of inward tranquillity which religion is powerless to bestow," and I am off on another goose chase.

Of course this is not one of Emerson's most serious utterances, but it is near enough to the bone to be uncomfortable. Shall I have to work harder to arouse the conscience of that woman in the pretty hat than of her neighbor in the shapeless felt? Do dowdy women respond more readily to the challenge of the gospel than smart ones? And is that why there are so many dowdy women in the pews of our churches? And that set me to thinking of Christina Rossetti, who was notoriously frumpish and ill-kempt, and of Dante Gabriel Rossetti's complaint that his sister's heart might indeed be like a singing bird, but her exterior was decidedly un-lyrical. And were the prophets of Israel afraid that women would dodge the issue if they got themselves up too attractively, hence their strictures on the use of cosmetics and bangles?

But clothes are not the only substitute for a good conscience. Men, too, have been known to find a "feeling of inward tranquillity" in such things as membership in a good club, hobnobbing with bishops, a substantial bank balance, the publication of a learned article, or the possession of an Oxford accent. In fact, there is no end to the ways in which people try to avoid making the confession, "Nothing in my hand I bring."

68

THE BIBLE CORRECTS ITS OWN HALF-TRUTHS. THE PROPHET who called upon Israel to "prepare . . . the way of the Lord" also urged them in another place to "prepare . . . the way of the people." But I find that most preachers are better at doing the first than the second. They pay more attention to upholding the righteousness of God than to understanding the difficulties of men. They are better at stating the answer than listening to the question. They devote more time and thought to presenting the Christian message than to investigating the needs of men.

A great deal of our preaching misses the target because we take it for granted that the needs of men are the same in every age. But are they? Has nothing happened, let us say in the last hundred years, to alter the shape of men's needs, their intensity, their balance? Jesus Christ is, indeed, the "same yesterday, and to day, and for ever," but is man the same? If we go on presenting Christ as the answer to man's problems, but fail to explore what those problems really are or blithely assume that they are the same in the mid-twentieth century as they were in the first century, is any wonder that our preaching is reckoned to be irrelevant?

There are, we are told, basic human needs—the needs for security, for love, for responsibility, for community, are some of them—but are they felt with the same intensity in each generation; do they press as urgently upon men in every age? Are the strains and stresses experienced by the human person in this technological civilization precisely the same as those experienced under the feudal system? The demands made by our twentieth-century Western society upon the resources of the human being must, it seems to me, condition the response that a man can make to the gospel. I am entirely of the opinion of Frederick Denison Maurice that the modern world seems to be producing a kind of man to whom the Christian gospel cannot be preached—but that is another subject! Much, I think, could be done still if we gave up repeating the parrot cry that the needs of man are constant and instead began to look at the men to whom we are preaching, at what life in a machine-dominated society is doing to human personality.

To go back no further than a hundred years, think what has happened to man in that time! Darwin, Marx, and Freud have each contributed to a new awareness of himself, questioned his traditional assumptions, and thrown him into uncertainty. The application of a scientific knowledge rather than science itself has shaped a new environment, to which man has to respond in a new way, setting up new stresses and conflicts within him.

Yet we go on talking the traditional language and using the traditional analysis of man. For example, we still talk as though the seven deadly sins as listed by the medieval Church corresponded to something real in modern life, and we even think that their order is sacrosanct. But is pride the first of the deadly sins in the modern world? It might have been in the Middle Ages in that age of violence and dramatic contrasts, of ostentatious show and choleric energy, but not surely in this age of "Lucky Jim." The "hero" of Kingsley Amis' best-selling novel is, alas, all too typical of our time, the young man with the benefits of state-aided grants, university education, security of employment, who positively *hates* greatness in any form, who is deliberately mediocre and self-effacing, whose interests are self-consciously trivial. To be proud today would be a positive virtue, not a sin. Man in the twentieth century needs to be recalled to his dignity as a human person, needs to be encouraged to assert himself. All this, of course, is perfectly consistent with true humility, but our modern life is bent on producing people who can only be servile, not truly humble.

It is a question not of nagging people, but of realizing first of all the enormous difficulty of making a truly religious response to life.

That response presupposes a personality capable of making it, and increasingly we find people becoming depersonalized, dehumanized, capable only of making what Martin Buber calls the I-it encounter with experience.

Isaiah's words, "Prepare ye the way of the people; cast up, cast up the highway; gather out the stones; lift up a standard for the people," are, I feel sure, capable of wide application in this generation and demand more consideration at this juncture in history than "Prepare ye the way of the Lord." It is a question of emphasis.

69

I TRIED OUT MY IDEAS ABOUT THE CHANGING NEEDS OF MAN AT A ministers' gathering this afternoon and got the response I expected. I was shouted down by half the men present as though I were making an attack upon the unchanging gospel. But Jack Hollis took me aside afterward and said, "I am not at all convinced that you are right, but go on, tell me more about these changing needs." Jack is always ready to listen to an idea, however unfamiliar or crack-brained it sounded at first hearing. That's what makes him such a delightful companion; you feel that you can think aloud in his presence. He is not always defending the gospel; he sometimes wants to understand it.

Of course, I agreed that the primary need, the need for God, remains constant. But the ways in which man experiences that need, and the response which he is capable of making to it, varies from age to age. The personality of man is tugged and pulled about in different ways under different conditions of living. He experiences the crises of life in different ways, at different times, with differing intensities. It is absurd to look upon man, I said, as though nothing had happened in the last fifty years in our Western, industrial society to alter the pattern of his emotional and instinctive life or to change the quality of his mind. It seems to me that there are at least five directions in which this change has taken place.

1. The school-leaving age has been raised. The period of childhood, of irresponsible adolescence, has been extended. When my father was a boy, he was working in a factory at the age of twelve. He was a wage earner, contributing to the household expenses; he was thrown every day into the company of men far older than himself, married men with families, men of skill and craft, men who both encouraged and rebuffed him when he needed it. Today a working-class lad leaves school at fifteen, and frequently stays until he is sixteen or seventeen. He makes no break from one society into another. Primitive societies all recognize the need for an abrupt break, for an initiation into a different type of society, at the age of puberty. The fact that this break does not now take place introduces its own strains and tensions in the personality of the growing lad.

2. The type of education given to children today is very different from that of fifty years ago. Boys and girls know a great deal more about a greater number of things. They are more sophisticated. Their attitude to life is more scientifically conditioned. They see life in terms of problem rather than in terms of mystery. Their response to life is more cerebral than instinctive.

3. The home has lost its place and power. It has become a

department of life alongside other departments, for example, school, work, the youth club. The parent-child relationship is much less full than it used to be. The authority of the parents has to compete with other authorities to a greater degree.

4. The choice of trade, profession, or vocation has been greatly widened. It is no longer taken for granted that Jack will follow in his father's footsteps, and therefore the father has nothing to teach his son in the way of a traditional craft or wisdom. It seems as if it is the aim of every modern parent to see that his son does *not* follow in his footsteps; he wants the boy to better himself, and this is possible in our grant-aided society with its greater choice of employment and the greater mobility of people. But it inevitably leads to a changed relationship between fathers and sons.

5. Greater mobility also means that people today do not have to adjust themselves to their immediate neighbors. If they don't like the people among whom they live, they can choose their friends from elsewhere. The problems of natural community living can be shelved; men tend to live in artificial communities made up of like-minded persons, sharing the same tastes and the same opinions. Thus the creative and disciplinary clash of convictions, temperaments, and so on is avoided.

6. The young person of today is stimulated to a far greater degree than were the adolescents of yesterday. His acquisitiveness is deliberately exploited by advertising; he is taught to want a greater number of things; his emotions are worked upon by films, the cheap press, even the advertisement hoardings. From all sides there is a terriffic assault upon his sexual nature.

This list could easily be extended, but all to the same purpose— to show that the promise and power of the gospel has to be presented so as to meet the needs of today, not the needs of another age. Salvation from sin is always necessary, but as Jean Guitton has said,

the sins of yesterday were like wounds inflicted by the sword; their contours were clean and the blood which flowed from the wound was healthy. Those of our own day might be likened rather to internal injuries, to those maladies which attack the cellular system.

And again,

What characterises this new age is a predominance of intellect over spontaneous life, of calculation over instinct, and in so far as sin is concerned, of aberration over guilt. Modern guilt envelops itself in a web of justification, compensation, sublimation, which makes it almost invisible to its subject.

Every generation finds in the gospel what is most significant for its peculiar needs. Luther, tuned to the spirit of his times, found in it justification by faith. Where is the Luther of the twentieth century?

70

TODAY I AM FIFTY. THANK GOODNESS I STILL HAVE MY HAIR; I don't look a day over forty-nine! But it's a solemn thought, and I celebrate by reading a poem. I take down Edwin Muir, whose *Collected Poems* are never far from my hand, and read again his moving "Soliloquy," written when he, too, I gather, had reached a responsible age.

> . . . I have picked up wisdom lying
> Disused about the world, available still,
> Employable still, small odds and scraps of wisdom . . .
> I have learned a host of little things, and one
> Too great for thinking, scarcely to be borne:
> That there's a watershed in human life,
> A natural mountain that we have to scale;
> And once at the top, our journey all lies downward,
> Down the long slope to age and sleep and the end
> (Sadder but easier than the hills of youth,
> And sometimes shot with gleams of sunset light).

> . . . I have learned another lesson:
> When life's half done you must give quality
> To the other half, else you lose both, lose all.
> Select, select: make an anthology
> Of what's been given you by bold casual time.
> Revise, omit; keep what's significant.
> Fill, fill deserted time. . . .

How to give quality to the other half, this is indeed my problem now. And I recall some lines from another modern poet, Cecil Day Lewis (New Year's Eve):

> But living becomes a habit, like any other
> No easier to break than to sanction . . .

And fast upon these come lines spoken by the shepherds in W. H. Auden's *For the Time Being,* "A Christmas Oratorio."

> Tonight for the first time the prison gates
> Have opened.

> Music and sudden light
> Have interrupted our routine tonight,
> And swept the filth of habit from our hearts.

There is an uncleanness that clings to the life which makes no fresh decisions, a scum that gets on the surface of life, which must be disturbed by conscious and deliberate choices, by action from within. So as I take up the fifty-first year, I resolve to break the crust of habit, to enjoy what has become routine, to cultivate the seeing eye, to cry with W. H. Davies:

> Lord!
> How rich and great the times are now!
> .   .   .   .
> A rainbow and a cuckoo's song
> May never come together again.

But it will be easier to do this with things than with people. The habit of taking people for granted, even unfortunately, one's own nearest and dearest, has to be resisted. The only line I remember from a recent novel is, "After ten years the marriage had settled down into a tired friendship." The good Lord preserve us from that. And preserve us, too, from taking ourselves for granted. Lloyd Pearsall Smith once declared that he was tired of waking up every morning the same old person. There is always the temptation of giving a good imitation of oneself, of repeating what has become easy and characteristic, of making automatic responses. Kierkegaard once said that to avoid becoming encrusted a man ought to imitate a good farmer. There is such a thing as rotation of crops in life as well as in agriculture.

I am realizing every day that the only way to avoid the "filth of habit" is to let God into one's life, to let him plow the living man from sleep. A radical encounter with Jesus Christ, who "makes all things new," is the only positive way to prevent living becoming a habit.

--------- *71* ---------

KNOWING MY HORROR OF THEOLOGICAL JARGON, THE YOUNG folk in the Youth Fellowship asked me tonight on the spur of the moment to tell them in simple, untechnical language what I believe. "How would you express your creed for someone who had never heard the language of the Bible or of the Church, who would be puzzled by such shorthand phrases as the love of God, the grace of Christ, and the power of the Spirit? To us such phrases mean something, even though they are apt to become cant phrases and substitutes for thought, but how would you express what they mean without using the phrases themselves?" This was a tall order, and they knew it. But at least they were a sympathetic audience!

The two strongest convictions of my life, the convictions upon which my life proceeds, are these: that I am responsible and that I belong. These two phrases sum up my creed. I am responsible to Someone other than myself, other than my friends and loved ones. There is a claim made upon my life. I feel that claim in varying degrees at various moments. Sometimes it is strongest in moments of failure. It is not myself that I have failed, not even those who depend upon me for human encouragement and help, but the Creator of my being. I feel it, again, in moments when life heaps its favors upon me. At the heart of every privilege and blessing there is a demand, a call for the response of gratitude and service. I feel it also, and at times most poignantly, in the presence of beauty of every sort. This is why beauty evokes tears from the eyes and has an undercurrent of sadness. One realizes that one is not worthy, that one is incapable of making the response demanded by the author of such beauty. I believe that I belong. My life as an individual is meaningless. I am only alive, only human, when I am a person in fellowship with other persons. But I belong not merely to people; I belong to the sum of things. I cannot by any stretch of the imagination say that I am only the creation of my parents or of society. I can repudiate both and yet not repudiate the One who created me.

But I am forever being tempted to be untrue to my deepest convictions. There is a pull on my life both from within and from without to evade responsibility and to avoid belonging. It is easier to accept the partial responsibilities, the limited responsibilities, of family and society than to accept the claim made upon my life by its Creator. It is less demanding to behave as though I were an individual than as if I were a person. This is what I call sin, taking the easy way out, accepting the short cut, the deliberate refusal to respond to life as a responsible and involved being.

For me Jesus of Nazareth stands out as the one who made the perfect response, which I am incapable of making. He was, to use a theological expression not much employed in this connection, the amen said to God, the full, free, deliberate response of man to his Creator. And that being so, he is the most representative man. All great men are representative men. All truly human beings, whether they be saints, artists, poets, scientists, or reformers, have an underlying conviction that they live, work,

173

struggle, discover, research, on behalf of humanity. It is this that sustains them and drives them. Their actions, their sacrifices, their heroism, are inexplicable on any other hypothesis. But inevitably some element of specialization enters into their lives; they are representative men in some capacity or another. Jesus of Nazareth was the Representative Man. He deliberately accepted and embraced that role. It is thus that he commands my loyalty and my love. By his life he has made my fuller response to God possible. From another point of view he has made it possible for God to treat me as the human being I have not yet become.

I believe that when I accept my status in life alongside Jesus Christ, when I live consciously and deliberately in the world that he has enlarged simply by being in it, my life becomes rich in creative possibilities. I am enabled to respond responsibly, not only as a moral being but as a human being, on all sides of my nature. I am enabled to enter into honest, deep, nondemanding relations with my fellow men and thus to create true community.

Something like this is what I said, and no one realizes its inadequacy more than I do. Given time, I could get to work on this rough statement, could polish up the phrases, correct the heresies, but I leave it here as it stands, an interim report, a statement forced out of me on the spur of the moment and doubtless more honest on that account.